Common Sense®
PARENTING

Learn-at-Home Workbook and DVD

Also from the Boys Town Press

Common Sense Parenting® DVD Series
>   Building Relationships
>   Teaching Children Self-Control
>   Preventing Problem Behavior
>   Correcting Misbehavior
>   Teaching Kids to Make Good Decisions
>   Helping Kids Succeed in School

Help! There's a Toddler in the House!

Great Days Ahead: Parenting Children Who Have ADHD with Hope and Confidence

Show Me Your Mad Face

Parenting to Build Character in Your Teen

Common Sense Parenting®

Common Sense Parenting® of Toddlers and Preschoolers

Raising Children without Losing Your Voice or Your Mind (DVD)

Adolescence and Other Temporary Mental Disorders (DVD)

Good Night, Sweet Dreams, I Love You: Now Get into Bed and Go to Sleep!

No Room for Bullies

The Well-Managed Classroom

Effective Study Strategies for Every Classroom

Safe and Healthy Secondary Schools

Competing with Character

The 100-Yard Classroom

Who's Raising Your Child?

Practical Tools for Foster Parents

There Are No Simple Rules for Dating My Daughter!

Teaching Social Skills to Youth with Mental Health Disorders

Changing Children's Behavior by Changing the People, Places, and Activities in Their Lives

Teaching Social Skills to Youth

Basic Social Skills for Youth

More Tools for Teaching Social Skills in School

Tools for Teaching Social Skills in School

Skills for Families, Skills for Life

Effective Skills for Child-Care Workers

Boundaries: A Guide for Teens

Getting Along with Others

Friend Me!

A Good Friend: How to Make One, How to Be One

Who's in the Mirror?

What's Right for Me?

BoysTownPress.org
For a free Boys Town Press catalog, call 1-800-282-6657

Common Sense® PARENTING

Learn-at-Home Workbook and DVD

RAY BURKE, PH.D.
RON HERRON
LINDA SCHUCHMANN, M.S.

BOYS TOWN®
Press

Boys Town, Nebraska

Common Sense Parenting®
Learn-at-Home DVD Workbook

Published by the Boys Town Press
Father Flanagan's Boys' Home
Boys Town, Nebraska 68010

ISBN 978-1-889322-60-5

 Boys Town Press is the publishing division of Boys Town, a national organization serving children and families.

15 14 13 12 11 10 9 8 7 6 5 4

Table of Contents

INTRODUCTION 1

CHAPTER 1   Parents Are Teachers 5

CHAPTER 2   Encouraging Positive Behavior 23

CHAPTER 3   Preventing Misbehavior 47

CHAPTER 4   Correcting Problem Behaviors. 67

CHAPTER 5   Handling Emotionally Intense Situations 89

CHAPTER 6   Helping Children Succeed in School 121

APPENDIX A   Joy Jar/Job Jar Suggestions 145

APPENDIX B   Social Skills 149

INDEX 169

Introduction

As a child, Andrea loved school, had plenty of friends, and always had a smile on her face. That all changed shortly after she started junior high. Over the past three years, Andrea has become, in her mother's words, "a surly, argumentative, and disrespectful brat who won't help around the house, refuses to do homework, and is just a pain to live with."

Marvin is one of those kids who is thinking of trouble on days when he isn't yet involved in it. By age 8, he already has been in more fights than any other kid on the block. Unfortunately, these fights are starting to occur at school where he has become a frequent visitor to the principal's office.

When folks at church comment, "What a cute smile!", Susan's mother is thinking, "They never would have said that if they saw this 5-year-old's two-hour tantrums at home!"

Mike, 16, was good about asking to use the car when he first started to drive. Now, instead of asking, Mike takes the car whenever he wants it. His parents don't know where he is half the time, and they're concerned about his safety when he's out late with friends.

Parenting is full of surprises – some pleasant, some frustrating, and some painful. Like most parents, those in the examples above have had no training or preparation for the issues they must deal with as their children mature. They rely on sheer persistence and determination to get through the painful moments, tactics learned from their own childhood to get through the frustrating times, and a brief pat on the back when pleasant surprises occur.

They all would appreciate some help along the way. That's why Boys Town developed the *Common Sense Parenting*® program: to help parents develop stronger relationships with their children and prevent many of the behavior problems that lead to difficulties at home and school.

Since 1989, a quarter of a million parents have participated in *Common Sense Parenting* classes in their communities. Research has shown that *Common Sense Parenting* helps parents reduce child behavior problems and improve their relationships with their children. Today, *Common Sense Parenting* (CSP) is available throughout the United States and in several foreign countries. Boys Town developed the *Common Sense Parenting Learn-At-Home* program to get information in a more convenient format to parents.

What makes *Common Sense Parenting* work so well? We emphasize two things: the "head" and the "heart." The "head" means using a logical, practical method of teaching your children; in other words, using skills to change your children's behavior. The "heart" means having unconditional love for your children. One without the other will not work. Put them both together and you have a powerful combination.

This program (whether in a class or on video) offers you a blueprint for parenting that emphasizes your role as your children's first and most important teacher. No one should have a greater impact on your children's lives than you. That means you have to bring to the task all the love, patience, skills, and energy you can muster. Through all of this, you will find that parenting is the most exciting challenge you will ever face. Make the most of it.

One last thing. All of the skills in this book rely on one crucial element of parenting. That element is spending time with your children. You can teach them only if you're with them. It's as simple as that. It's absolutely, positively a must that you spend time talking with them, listening to them, encouraging them, finding out what they're doing and what's important to them, and helping them learn to be safe. If there is one secret to parenting, it's that there is no substitute for the time and love you give your children.

How to Use This Book

This workbook can be used with either the CSP classes or *Learn-At-Home* program. Chapters correspond to both the six class sessions and the six 30-minute video segments in the kit. At the end of each chapter are exercises for either the class or the kit. Each exercise has a small picture in the upper left hand corner of the page that lets you know whether the exercise is for class or the kit. We would encourage you to complete class assignments after each class. Kit assignments can be completed when you are viewing the section of the video that corresponds to the exercise.

Kit Exercise

Class Exercise

Parents have told us that they get so much out of CSP classes because they get an hour of practice in each two-hour class. That practice gives parents the chance to use the skills in less-threatening situations before using the skills in real-life situations with their children.

Parents who are watching the video don't have that opportunity to practice using the skill with other parents or their own personal trainer. So, if you are using this workbook with the video, we encourage you to watch the video several times, do the exercises as described, and practice using the skills before jumping into situations with your children. When problems occur, or you don't feel comfortable with how you handled a situation with your children, read or view the related material once again. If problems persist or you would like some additional help, call the Boys Town National Hotline at 1-800-448-3000. Counselors are available 24 hours a day, every day.

We fully realize that there are no perfect answers to the problems parents face with their children. Each situation, each parent, and each child is unique. For that reason, we offer you practical techniques, guidelines, and suggestions that can easily be adapted into your own style of interacting with your children. The *Common Sense Parenting* techniques have been successfully used with children from 3 to 16 years of age. Be sure to adapt these techniques to fit the age and developmental level of your children.

Just one note about the change process. Change takes time. The behaviors your children now display are a result of all the learning they have experienced in their lives. Learning new behaviors won't occur overnight. Things often get worse before they get better. It's much like remodeling a house. You live with a lot of dust and dirt before you ever have things the way you want them. At times, you may feel like throwing up your hands and saying, "What's the use?" We encourage you not to give up. Just like with remodeling, you can complete the task at hand through patience, hard work, and perseverance.

Expect some pitfalls. Understand that it takes time and effort. Learn to look at each improvement as a step in the right direction. Pat yourself on the back when you conquer a problem with one of your kids. The moments of self-doubt you experience will eventually be replaced with a renewed confidence in your parenting abilities. What's more, you will feel a positive sense of direction in how you teach your children.

There are no magical cures for the problems parents face. But the skills in this book have helped thousands of parents deal with and prevent the situations that trouble many families. We hope you, like so many other parents, find these skills to be practical, useful, and beneficial.

CHAPTER 1

Parents Are Teachers

Discipline is often misunderstood. As parents, we may each take a different approach to discipline. This may include punishment, correction, and/or guidance.

In this chapter, we'll be learning about:

➤ Discipline

➤ Clear communication

➤ Using consequences to change behavior

Discipline

What comes to mind when you think of the word "discipline?" Jot some of your thoughts on the following lines.

Discipline is _____

_____

When my parents disciplined me, they _____

_____

_____

When I discipline my kids, I_____

_____

_____

ACTIVITY 1

Identify which of the following is discipline by teaching and which is discipline by punishment.

1 Mike is playing with the TV video game. Johnny doesn't want to wait his turn, so he walks up and unplugs the game. Mike hits him with a Ping-Pong paddle. Mom hears what's going on, grabs Mike, shakes him, and yells, "Don't you dare hit your brother like that!"

Teaching or Punishment ?

2 Sally and her friend are talking about the new girl in school. Mom overhears Sally tell her friend that they shouldn't play with the new girl any more because she doesn't wear neat clothes. Mom asks the girls to sit down and they talk about how clothes shouldn't determine how someone feels about another person. Mom says it is what's inside a person that is important, not what's on the outside.

Teaching or Punishment ?

3 Felicia draws a picture on the living room wall with a red crayon. She finds Mom, shows her the picture, and asks her if she likes it. Mom spanks Felicia and sends her to her room for an hour.

Teaching or Punishment ?

4 Dad tells Ty that he can't go shoot baskets because he has homework to finish. Ty gets angry, stomps his feet, and complains how unfair his father is. Dad tells Ty that they need to talk about Ty's behavior. First, he says that Ty needs to calm down and stop yelling. Moments later, after Ty has settled down, Dad explains to Ty how to accept "No" for an answer.

Teaching or Punishment ?

(Answers: 1 & 3 Punishment, 2 & 4 Teaching)

Here's what some parents have told us:

➤ Discipline was when my parents sent me to my room all day when I was in trouble.

➤ Discipline was when my parents would give me a whipping.

➤ Discipline was when my parents would lecture me. I hated that.

➤ Discipline reminds me of yelling, spankings, and getting on my kids' backs.

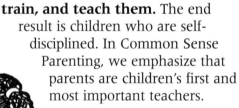

TIP... The dictionary defines discipline as education, training, and teaching.

If you think of discipline in these terms, you probably see discipline as something negative. If so, you're not alone. Most parents, as a recent survey on parenting indicated, use punitive or unpleasant responses when their children misbehave. This means parents yell, scold, call their kids names, or use physical punishment. While discipline by punishment occurs often, punishment is not the best way to discipline children.

As parents, it is our job to discipline our children, that is, we need to educate, train, and teach them. The end result is children who are self-disciplined. In Common Sense Parenting, we emphasize that parents are children's first and most important teachers.

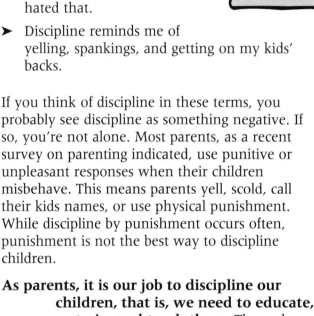

Clear Communication

Good teachers use clear communication. As parents, that means we must clearly and accurately describe our children's behavior.

Behavior is anything a person does that can be seen or heard.

Do children really understand what their parents mean when they make statements like these:

"You're a real brat; you're very disrespectful."

"You've got a lousy attitude!"

"Shape up and stop being so naughty."

"You were a good boy at the store."

TIP... Communicate clearly with children. Describe their behavior – what they say and do.

To be effective teachers for our children, we must clearly communicate with them. Words like "brat," "disrespectful," "lousy attitude," "naughty," and "good boy," are not clear and concrete. For kids, this can be confusing and frustrating.

Here are some specific descriptions of behavior:

➤ My son throws his books down and says that he won't do his homework.

➤ My son helped put away the dishes and wiped the table.

➤ When I asked my son to take out the trash, he argued and complained about having to do it.

➤ My daughter talks on the phone for one hour at a time.

➤ When I ask my son to do something, he rolls his eyes and walks away.

➤ When my kids come home from school, they put their books away and ask if there's anything that needs to be done around the house.

➤ When I tell my daughter her jeans are too tight, she whines and asks me why I am always on her back.

When we specifically describe our children's behaviors, they understand what they've done right or wrong. When they know what they've done correctly, they can do things right more often in the future. When they know what

---

ACTIVITY 2

Circle the statements that give clear messages.

1. Billy, why can't you act your age when we have company?

2. Veronica, keep your mouth closed when you chew your food.

3. When we go to the store, please be a nice girl.

4. Jim, would you please rake the backyard, put the leaves in a big plastic bag, and put the bag on the front curb?

5. That was a nice story you wrote for English class, Sam.

6. Sally, you need to stop talking right now.

7. Reggie, don't eat like a pig!

8. Chuck, after school you are to come right home. Don't stop to play. And call me at work when you get home.

9. Billy, thanks for sitting still and not talking in church.

(Answers: Clear messages: 2, 4, 6, 8, 9
Confusing Messages: 1, 3, 5, 7)

Time-Out

Here's how it works.

Immediately following a problem behavior, describe that behavior to your child and send (or take) him or her to Time-Out. Do not threaten or spank. Avoid giving your child a lot of attention at this time.

How do I set up Time-Out with my kids?

Before you ever begin using Time-Out, explain to your child what Time-Out is, which problem behaviors it will be used for, and how long it will last. For example, you could say, "When I ask you to put your toys away and you start crying and throwing your toys, you will have to go sit on a chair in the kitchen for three minutes. When you stop crying and sit quietly, I'll start the timer. When the timer buzzes, you can get up." Then practice having your child go to the chair when you ask.

Have a convenient place for your Time-Out area. It doesn't have to be the same place each time. A kitchen chair, a couch, a footstool, or a step will work. Make sure the area is safe, well lit, and free from "fun" distractions like the TV or toys.

How long should children stay in Time-Out?

As a general rule, a child should spend one quiet minute in Time-Out for every year of his or her age up to a maximum of five minutes. So, if your child is three years old, the longest amount of quiet time he should spend is three minutes. If your child is five years old, Time-Out should last no longer than five minutes. Even if your child is seven years old, she should not sit for more than five minutes after she has started Time-Out.

During Time-Out, your child is to be quiet and sit calmly in the chair. Time spent complaining, crying, or throwing a tantrum does not count
(continued on page 9)

they've done wrong, they have a clearer idea of what not to do. But knowledge alone doesn't always mean that children will change their behavior. So, what do we need to do to help our children change their behavior? We need to combine our teaching with consequences.

Using Consequences to Change Behavior

Consequences teach children to think and to learn that their actions lead to results, both positive and negative. Adults face consequences every day. If we don't get our work done, the boss criticizes us. If we compliment a friend, he speaks pleasantly to us.

You've probably used consequences many times before; for example, "grounding" your child for coming home late is a common consequence parents use. But simply giving a consequence doesn't automatically cause kids to change their behavior. Parents need to combine clear messages and consequences when teaching children. This combination, coupled with love and affection, is very effective.

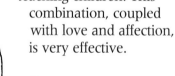

There are two kinds of consequences – positive and negative.

Positive consequences are things people like and are willing to work to get. Behavior that is followed by a positive consequence is more likely to occur again. Rewards and privileges are forms of positive consequences.

Negative consequences are things people don't like and want to avoid. Behavior that is followed by a negative consequence is less likely to occur again (or will not occur as frequently). We recommend two types of negative consequences for misbehavior – taking away a privilege and adding chores.

Negative Consequences: Taking Away a Privilege

For young children, taking away privileges for short amounts of time can be very effective. One way of doing this is called "Time-Out." It is a way of disciplining young children without raising your hand or your voice. Time-Out involves having your child sit in one place, away from all distractions, for a certain amount of time. (Be sure to read the section on Time-Out, pages 8-9, for more specific information about how to use it with your children.)

TIP...
There are two types of negative consequences – taking away a privilege and adding chores.

For older children, taking away a privilege when a problem behavior occurs is generally an effective consequence. For example, if your two children are arguing over what TV show to watch, they could lose TV privileges for an hour. Or, if your daughter ignores you when you ask her to get off the telephone, she could lose her telephone privileges for 30 minutes. Or, if your teenage daughter comes home an hour late, you may remove part of a privilege. You could say to her, "Sarah, because you're one hour late, your curfew will be one hour earlier tomorrow night." If coming home on time is a frequent problem, she may lose the privilege of going out next time: "Sarah, because you've been late the last three times you went out with friends, you won't be able to go out tomorrow night at all."

(Time-Out continued from page 8)
toward quiet time. On the other hand, fidgeting and talking in a soft voice probably should count. If you start the time because your child is quiet but then he starts to cry or throw a tantrum again, wait until he is quiet and start the time over again.

What if my kids leave before their time is finished?

Your child should remain seated and quiet to leave Time-Out. If he decides he's had enough and leaves the chair too early, calmly return him to the chair. If this happens several times (and it often does when you first begin using Time-Out), keep returning your child to the chair.

If you get tired or other activities take you away from the Time-Out area, you can tell your child to leave the chair and give a different consequence. Your child may lose the privilege of playing with a toy or watching TV, or friends may have to go home. At a time when your child is calm, practice using Time-Out again. Practice often enough that your child begins staying in the chair in actual Time-Out situations.

When you first start using Time-Out, it's very likely that your child will cry, say some nasty things, throw toys, or make a mess. Ignore anything that is not dangerous to your child, you, or your home. Most negative behavior is an attempt to get you to change your mind about using Time-Out.

What do I do when Time-Out is finished?

When the Time-Out period is over, ask your child, "Are you ready to get up?" Your child must answer "Yes" in a way that is agreeable to you – a nod or an "Okay" works just fine. Then you can say that Time-Out is over and your child can return to his or her play activities. We'll talk about other teaching you can do after Time-Out is finished in the chapter on Corrective Teaching later in the book.

Here's a list of possible chores for your children.

- Folding laundry
- Putting laundry away
- Making a brother's or sister's bed
- Vacuuming one or several rooms
- Raking all or part of the yard
- Mowing the grass
- Cleaning out a kitchen drawer
- Helping a brother or sister with chores
- Collecting all the trash in the house
- Taking out the trash
- Dusting furniture
- Sweeping the porch
- Washing some or all of the windows
- Washing the car
- Cleaning out the car
- Washing the car windows (inside)
- Cleaning out the garage
- Organizing a closet
- Helping a brother or sister put toys away
- Washing, drying, or putting away the dishes
- Sweeping the kitchen or dining room
- Cleaning the bathroom
- Cleaning the kitchen sink
- Shaking the rugs

Negative Consequences: Adding Chores

Adding chores is another effective method for teaching responsibility. In some instances, the chore can be directly related to the problem. For example, your son can vacuum the carpet after he tracks dirt into the house.

TIP... Adding chores that are not related to the misbehavior can be an effective negative consequence.

Chores that are not related to the behavior can be just as effective at changing a negative behavior. For example, if your children are fighting over a toy, the consequence could be that they fold a load of laundry together. While this chore is not directly related to fighting over the toy, folding laundry together gives them an opportunity to learn how to get along with each other.

Here are a couple of examples of how chores can be used as consequences for kids:

➤ Your son breaks a friend's bike. To teach him responsibility, you tell him he must earn money to pay for repairing the bike by doing extra chores around the home.

➤ Your daughters are arguing about who gets to use the phone. Their consequence is to clean the bathroom together and discuss how they can take turns on the phone.

Add chores that are different from the chores your children normally do as part of their family responsibilities. When using chores as consequences, be sure to take into account the age and ability of your children.

The Job Jar and Joy Jar

Sometimes it's challenging to come up with meaningful positive or negative consequences on the spur of the moment. The Job and Joy Jars give parents a quick and easy supply of consequences that are always available.

One way to use chores as a consequence is to make a Job Jar. Parents and children write various chores on small pieces of paper and put them in a jar. When a child misbehaves, the parent has the child select a chore from the jar. It works best if parents tell their kids ahead of time about the job jar and how it will work.

Use the Joy Jar the same way you use the Job Jar. You and your children can write things they like to do on small slips of paper. (There are lots of good ideas for positive consequences for the Joy Jar throughout this chapter.) Put the slips in a jar. Then, when your child does something well, you can have him or her get something out of the Joy Jar. Suggestions for Job and Joy Jar consequences are listed in Appendix A.

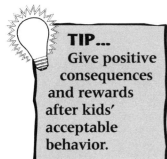

TIP...
Give positive consequences and rewards after kids' acceptable behavior.

Positive Consequences

Positive consequences can be a parent's best friend because they can be used to increase positive behavior. Positive consequences can also be called rewards. Generally, rewards are things that people like or enjoy. Therefore, when we use the term "reward," we mean any type of consequence that makes behavior occur again.

Are you giving a negative consequence?

Sometimes, parents make the mistake of assuming that a consequence is negative when it isn't. We encourage you to look at the effect a consequence has on the behavior you want to change. If the behavior stops or decreases in frequency, you've given a negative consequence. If the behavior continues or occurs more often, you've given a positive consequence.

For example, one mother told us that her six-year-old continually fidgeted and talked in church. She told him that he couldn't come with her next time if he continued causing problems in church. Sure enough, the son fidgeted and talked more than ever. He didn't want to be in church, and his mother had given him a positive consequence for his misbehavior.

We suggested that she do one of the following:

➤ **Remove a privilege** – if her son fidgets and talks in church, he can't play with his friend after church.

➤ **Add a chore** – if he fidgets or talks in church, he has to help Mom clean the kitchen.

Actually, the mother used a combination of both methods. If her son fidgeted and talked in church, he couldn't play with his friend until he finished helping in the kitchen. It worked. The young boy learned to sit quietly in church.

Bribes

To some parents, giving rewards to kids seems like bribing them for doing what they're expected to do. There is a difference between rewards and bribes.

It's bribery when parents give positive consequences to stop children's misbehavior. For example, giving a child a candy bar when he's crying and screaming in the grocery store in order to get him to be quiet is a bribe. If this occurs frequently enough, the child will expect something before he'll behave as the parent wants.

We want to give positive consequences and rewards after kids' acceptable behavior – behavior that we want to see again. So be sure to give positive consequences only for positive behavior, and after the desired behavior occurs.

Types of Positive Consequences

The following list summarizes a variety of positive consequences that parents have used with their children.

Activities – What everyday and special activities does your child like to do? For example, ride bikes, play outside, talk on the phone, watch TV, play video games or sports, bake cookies, read, go to a ball game or movie, visit the zoo, have a friend stay overnight.

Possessions – What kind of material articles does your child like? For example, toys, team athletic wear, video games, sweatshirts, baseball cards, comic books, dolls, music cassettes or CDs.

Food (or food activities such as helping make the meal or picking out the cereal) – What are your child's favorite foods and beverages? For example, candy, pop, ice cream, popcorn, pizza, soda, cookies, fruit juice. In terms of consequences, "food" refers to special snacks or treats. *(Do NOT use meals as a consequence. For example, do not take away a balanced meal and make your child eat bread and water. Children have the right to proper nutrition.)*

People – With whom does your child like to spend time? For example, you, friends, grandparents, cousins, schoolteachers.

Attention – What specific kinds of verbal and physical attention from you and others does your child like? For example, hugs, smiles, time with you, compliments, high-fives, thumbs up, and praise.

Using the examples as a guide, identify things your children like and write them on the homework assignment at the end of this chapter. Keep the list handy until you have a pretty good idea about which positive consequences are most effective with your child.

Some parents think they must buy something as a reward every time a child behaves well. This isn't so. Positive attention, praise, and encouragement are some of the most effective positive consequences a parent has – and they cost nothing!

Remember, the more you use positive consequences, the more likely you are to see positive behavior. The most powerful reward for children can be praise and positive attention from you.

Choosing a Consequence

What should you consider when choosing a consequence for your child's behavior?

➤ **The consequence has to be important to your child.** Taking away or giving a privilege that doesn't interest your child will not help change behavior. For example, if your daughter likes to borrow your earrings, then the earrings are important to her. This makes the earrings an effective positive or negative consequence. Also watch what your children do during their free time. Let's say your son likes to invite friends to your house, watch cartoons, and ride his bicycle. These everyday privileges and special activities can be effective positive or negative consequences for him.

> **TIP...**
>
> Consequences should be the right size, important, immediate, and linked to the behavior.

➤ **Consequences are more effective if they occur immediately after the child's behavior.** So, if you are trying to encourage your daughter to get her homework completed each evening, use a positive consequence that takes place right after she finishes her homework. This consequence could be playing cards with her, letting her talk on the phone, or doing something else she likes to do.

The following list includes positive consequences that are inexpensive and easy to use.

- Having an indoor picnic
- Staying up late
- Staying out later (set time)
- Having a messy room for a day
- Going over to a friend's house
- Leaving the radio on at night
- Picking the TV program
- Having a friend over
- Picking an outing
- Sleeping downstairs or outside
- Playing game with parent(s)
- Playing a video game
- Reading a story
- Doing one less chore
- Sleeping late on weekends
- Fishing with parents
- Picking a movie
- Having extra phone time
- Planning a meal
- Taking a trip to the library
- Going to a special event
- Having extra computer time
- Picking breakfast cereal at the store
- Going window shopping

➤ **Parents should be aware of the size of the consequence and try to give the smallest consequence they think will work.** Giving large positive consequences for minor behaviors may result in a "spoiled" child – one who gets too much for doing too little. On the other hand, giving large negative consequences for small misbehaviors may result in children who feel punished and resentful. Eventually, these children may try to avoid being around their parents altogether. For example, if your two children are arguing, having them clean the whole house may be too large a consequence. Having them fold a load of laundry takes less time and may be more appropriate.

➤ **When parents clearly link the consequence to the behavior, it will be more effective.** This is often called "Grandma's Rule." You remember Grandma's Rule – "First you eat your vegetables, then you get dessert." The same works for other behaviors. For example, if you want the dishes washed

> **TIP...**
> Your praise and attention are two of the most powerful positive consequences you can use – and they cost nothing!

and your daughter wants to talk on the phone, then link the consequence (talking on the phone) to the behavior (washing the dishes.) She has to finish the dishes before she can talk on the phone. You may be eating from dirty plates for weeks if you allow her to call friends before washing the dishes! Here's another situation: Your daughter wants to go to the movies and you want her to come home from school on time. When she comes home from school on time for a whole week, then you can take her to the movies. If you take her to the movies before she comes home on time for a week, then she's less likely to come home promptly from school.

When Consequences Don't Work

Occasionally, parents tell us that the consequences they used didn't work with their kids. It is possible that these children have problems that are too severe for parents to handle. In that case, they may need to see a professional counselor.

There are other reasons, however, why consequences don't work:

➤ **Some parents give many more negative consequences than positive.** As a result, the kids look elsewhere for positive consequences because it's too unpleasant to be around their parents.

➤ **Parents don't always allow enough time for consequences to work.** Your kids learned to behave the way they do over a long period of time. Be patient and watch for small improvements that result from the consequences you use.

➤ **Some parents mistake privileges for rights.**
The rights of kids include the right to
nourishment, communication with others,
and clothing. Such things as watching TV,
going out with friends, receiving
allowance, and using family
possessions are privileges that
should be earned by the child with a
parent's approval and supervision.

TIP...
**Be patient
and look
for small
improvements.**

It's wise to plan ahead and set
up both positive and negative
consequences in advance (for
example, the Job Jar and Joy Jar). Consequences
shouldn't be surprises. It's only fair to make your
kids aware of what they will earn for behaving
well and what they will lose for misbehaving.

Helpful Hints

When delivering a consequence, remember the following:

➤ **Be clear.** Make sure your child knows what the
consequence is and what he or she did to earn it.

➤ **Follow through.** If your child earns a positive
consequence, be sure you provide it for him or
her. Likewise, if you give a negative
consequence, don't let your child talk you out
of it. If you later feel that what you did was
unreasonable or done out of anger, apologize
and adjust the consequence accordingly.

➤ **Use a variety of consequences.** Instead of
grounding your children every time they tease
and fight with each other, you can have them
do a chore together, help each other with
schoolwork, lose a privilege, or earn any
number of other consequences.

➤ **Don't lecture.** This is especially true with
younger children.

The Avalanche Trap

One problem with negative
consequences is that parents can
lose sight of when to stop giving
them. If one consequence doesn't
work, parents try another and
another, each one harsher than
the last, until there's an avalanche
of consequences.

For example, Amy's dad asked
her to clean her room. She didn't,
so her dad took away her telephone privileges for a weekend.
Her room was still messy the
next day. For this, she lost a week
of TV privileges. The room didn't
get any cleaner and her father got
angrier and more frustrated. So
he added another month without
phone privileges, and another
week without TV, and told her
that she could not come out of
her room until it was spotless.

Since the consequences given by
this father were unreasonable (and
nearly impossible for Dad to
enforce), we suggested that he go
back, talk to Amy, and set up the
following plan:

1. Dad helps Amy clean her room.

2. In return, Amy helps Dad clean
the garage.

If both parts of the plan are
completed, Amy gets her privileges back. To help Amy keep the
room clean consistently, we
helped the father put a new plan
into practice: Each day that Amy
cleans her room, she gets to use
the phone and watch her favorite
TV show. If her room is not clean,
then no phone or TV until she
cleans her room. This arrangement keeps Dad from getting
caught in the avalanche trap, and it
gives Amy a fresh chance each day.

➤ **Avoid warnings.** Warnings mean you are merely threatening to give consequences. For example, if you say, "The next time you two argue about what TV show to watch, I'm going to turn it off for the rest of the evening," then you're warning them. You're telling them what you'll do the next time they argue. When you warn or threaten to give consequences, you and your consequences lose effectiveness. Instead of warning, give a consequence right away. Then your kids will know that you mean what you say.

➤ **Watch your behavior when you give the consequence.** Be pleasant and enthusiastic when giving positive consequences. Be calm and matter-of-fact when giving negative consequences. Yelling and screaming are not effective when giving negative consequences. Kids won't hear your words if they can only hear your anger.

Summary

Discipline involves teaching children self-discipline. To be good teachers parents need to be clear in their communication with their children. That's why it's important to describe children's behavior – what they say or do that you see or hear. When parents describe behavior, children are more likely to understand what they've done well or what they need to change to improve their behavior.

If parents want to change children's behavior, they need to link the behavior to positive or negative consequences. In the next chapters, we'll cover more information about how to combine clear messages with positive consequences to encourage positive behavior. We'll also learn how to combine clear messages and negative consequences when children misbehave.

Questions and Comments from Parents

Q. If my kid is lazy, what's wrong with telling him he is lazy?

A. Telling a child that he is lazy doesn't tell him what he is doing wrong or how to change his behavior. Instead of calling him lazy, specifically describe what he is or is not doing. For example, you might say, "Leo, you've been laying on the couch for the last hour. Please turn off the TV and get started on your homework."

Q. I don't have enough money to keep giving my kid some of these consequences. What should I do?

A. Consequences don't have to cost anything. Activities, attention, and privileges are consequences that do not cost money. Your positive attention is one of the best consequences you can give your children – and it costs nothing!

Q. My child already knows how to clean his room. Why should I have to specifically describe it to him?

A. If he already knows, you may not have to describe it to him. On the other hand, if he's not sure, make a specific list of tasks needed to get his room clean. Then make a chart or contract (Chapter 2) to help him and you keep track of how he's doing. Specific descriptions let kids know exactly what you want or exactly what they're doing well so they can continue those behaviors.

Q. You talk about using "special snacks" as a consequence. But I don't agree with my kids having anything other than fruit for snacks, and they get fruit anytime they want. What should I do?

A. That's fine. Use other types of consequences. There are examples of various types of consequences throughout this chapter.

Q. I've tried every type of consequence I can think of and none of them work. What now?

A. Parents occasionally tell us this. Sometimes, you may need to seek out a counselor to help with the problem. But before you do, go back and see how you've been using consequences. Answering the following questions will help you.

- Is the consequence the right size?
- When the problem behavior occurs, does the consequence follow soon afterward?
- How important is the consequence to your child?
- How long have you been using the consequence?
- Are you measuring small improvements in your child's behavior or are you expecting the problem to be corrected right away?

Q. Shouldn't kids do some things just because they're supposed to? My parents never rewarded me for doing chores; they just tanned my hide if I didn't!

A. It would be nice if kids did things such as cleaning their room, coming home on time, and picking up after themselves just because you expect them to, but sometimes they don't. When they don't, then use consequences and the teaching we describe in the following chapters to encourage them to start doing these things. Once children learn and show you they can continue these behaviors on their own, you can decrease the use of consequences.

Q. I can't afford to buy anything for the consequences, and my child just wants new gym shoes. What should I do?

A. Many parents face a similar situation. But you don't need to purchase things for your kids every time they do something well. Praise them when they do well, and when you want to provide additional incentives for your kids, have them earn something. For example, your child could do extra chores around the home and earn money to put toward new gym shoes. Or he could ask around the neighborhood to see if anyone else needs help. Teach him how to work and save for the new shoes. Then use other consequences such as your time and attention to encourage positive behavior.

Q. What consequences work best for little kids?

A. Little kids like attention (hugs and time with you) and activities (reading books, playing blocks). Be sure to give a consequence immediately after the behavior because it helps young children make the connection between their behavior and what they get to do.

Q. What consequences work best for 17- and 18-year-olds?

A. Older kids and teens like time with friends, and free time to use privileges such as talking on the telephone, going places, and getting rides or using the car. They also can work to earn money that they can use for new clothing or special activities.

Remember, even though teens may spend a majority of their time at school and with friends, arrange your schedule for them to spend time with you. Whether it's a late night chat about the day's activities or a special time once a week; make time for those ever-busy older children. That time together can be the best positive consequence for your teen.

Exercise 1 – Describing Children's Behavior

Watch the children in each video scene. Then, circle the clearest description of the child's behavior.

Scene 1

This parent might describe his son's behavior by saying:
a.   Now, this is a miracle!
b.   Nice job being responsible.
c.   Thanks for getting your homework done.
d.   Who are you and what have you done with my son?

Scene 2

To clearly describe the children's behavior, a parent could say:
a.   You kids are slobs.
b.   You kids have left your toys and clothes laying around.
c.   This place looks like a pig sty!
d.   You know better than this.

Scene 3

In this example, a parent might say:
a.   You are ignoring me.
b.   Knock off that attitude.
c.   Get back here. I know you heard me!
d.   Where do you think you're going?

Scene 4

In this example, the little girl is:
a.   Being a brat.
b.   Being a pest.
c.   Getting on mom's nerves.
d.   Whining and begging for a cookie.

Exercise 2 – Giving Consequences

 After watching each video example, circle the consequence that is likely to be most effective. Remember, consequences should follow the behavior and be immediate, important to the child, and the right size.

Scene 1

A good consequence for this arguing is:
- a. Throw the coloring book away.
- b. No coloring for 30 minutes.
- c. Ground them for 6 months.
- d. Tell them they're acting like babies.

Scene 2

An effective negative consequence for Michael would be:
- a. Shut off the TV and send him to bed.
- b. Let him stay up longer if he promises to be quiet.
- c. Threaten to take away TV for a week if he doesn't stop arguing.
- d. Stuff cotton in your ears and ignore him.

Scene 3

To reward Anthony for finishing his homework, this father should:
- a. Give him $20.
- b. Promise to do something together later in the week.
- c. Say "Why can't you do this all of the time?"
- d. Praise him for doing his homework.

Scene 4

To discourage this behavior a parent could:
- a. Yell at them to "knock it off."
- b. Warn them not to break anything.
- c. Threaten to "tan their hides."
- d. Give them an extra chore.

Homework 1 – Identifying Behaviors and Consequences

Please write specific behavioral descriptions of four positive and four negative behaviors for children in your family. In the space next to each behavior write a consequence that you used, or could have used, after the behavior.

Positive Behavior | Consequence

1. _____

2. _____

3. _____

4. _____

1. _____

2. _____

3. _____

4. _____

Negative Behavior | Consequence

1. _____

2. _____

3. _____

4. _____

1. _____

2. _____

3. _____

4. _____

Homework 2 – Selecting Effective Consequences

 In the spaces below, please write specific consequences that you could use with your children.

1. **Activities** – What everyday or special activities do your children like to do? For example, do they like playing video games, watching television, playing with friends, or going to the zoo?

   _____

   _____

   _____

2. **Possessions** – What kinds of material articles do your children like? For example, do they like books, clothes, baseball cards, money, toys, or music cassettes?

   _____

   _____

   _____

3. **Food** – What are your children's favorite foods or food activities? For example, do they like popcorn, popsicles, pizza, cola, candy, waffles, granola bars, or fruit juices? Or do they like to make cookies or help with grocery shopping?

   _____

   _____

   _____

4. **People** – With whom do your children spend time? For example, do they like to spend time with you, their grandparents, or friends?

   _____

   _____

   _____

5. **Attention** – What specific kinds of verbal and physical attention do your children like? For example, do your children like hugs, smiles, compliments, high-fives, thumbs-up, and praise?

   _____

   _____

   _____

CHAPTER 2

Encouraging Positive Behavior

In this chapter, we'll be learning about ways to help encourage our children's positive behavior. We'll be learning about:

➤ **General praise and affection**

➤ **"Effective Praise"**

➤ **Using charts and contracts to help children set and reach reasonable goals**

General Praise and Affection

There are many things we can do to encourage our children's positive behavior. One of the easier ways is to get in the habit of showing affection and complimenting our children.

We can show our affection in many different ways. For example, we can smile at our children, hug and hold them, or give them high-fives, pats on the back, or the old thumbs-up sign. We also can show our affection by helping our children, spending time with them, playing with them, teaching them to do things around the house, or just doing silly but fun things with them, such as having everyone camp out in the family room.

The easiest way to praise children is to say things like, "Fantastic," "Great," or "Keep up the good work," when they do something well. This is what we call general praise. General praise is typically vague, but positive. These words show your affection and approval, and encourage your kids to do even more things well in the future.

ACTIVITY 1

Affection and Praise

Write five examples of ways you show affection for your child.

1. _____

   _____

2. _____

   _____

3. _____

   _____

4. _____

   _____

5. _____

   _____

When parents spend time with their children and show them affection, they're building strong relationships and encouraging positive behavior.

Here are some examples of general praise other parents have used.

- "Awesome!"
- "Holy Cow!"
- "That's amazing!"
- "Will you look at that!"
- "You really did your best!"
- "I wish I could do that!"
- "Way to go!"
- "Out of this world!"
- "Terrific!"
- "Incredible!"
- "Wow!"
- "I knew you could do it!"

While general praise is helpful, you can make it even better. By adding a couple of key words, you can help your children clearly understand what they've done well. That's why we make a distinction between general praise and what we call "Effective Praise."

Effective Praise

Effective Praise is telling our children, in a specific way, what they do well. Effective Praise is especially helpful when you want to help your child learn and use specific positive behaviors.

When to Use Effective Praise

Use Effective Praise any time your child does well and you want to see that behavior occur more often in the future. Focus on the following areas when looking for opportunities to praise your children.

1. **Look for things your kids already do well.** Your children may already get up on time, or clean their rooms, or turn off the lights when they leave a room. Praise them for these behaviors and they will, most likely, continue to do these things.

What are some things your children already do well? _____

_____

_____

_____

2. **Make sure you recognize when your kids are making improvements, no matter how small.** For example, your child might have a history of not doing his homework. If he starts bringing his books home, but still isn't consistently getting his homework completed, praise him for bringing his work home. Then set up a plan for helping him get his homework started and completed. Praise small steps in the right direction any time your children are making improvements. They may not be good at the task, but they're getting better.

What are some improvements your children are making? _____

_____

_____

_____

3. **Praise positive attempts to do new things.** When your kids are learning new skills, they may be more likely to stick with the process if you praise them for their positive attempts to learn the new skill. For example, praise your children if they introduce themselves to a new coach, or sound out a new word rather than ask you for help. Your enthusiasm and attention to your children's attempts at success can carry over to many areas of their lives, regardless of age.

What are some activities your child has recently tried for the first time? _____

_____

_____

_____

Accentuate the Positive!

One parent commented, "Why is it so easy to pick out the negative things our children do? I don't miss a chance to get on my kids' back but it feels funny to praise them for things they do right ."

It's easy to see the mistakes and shortcomings of our children. As a society, we tend to focus on the negative things around us. Just read the newspaper or watch the evening news. Most of the information tells us about the problems in our world. We have learned to see the negative things around us, so while it may not be pleasant, we're comfortable with it.

That's why we often feel awkward when we point out that our children are doing things well. Focusing on their positive behaviors is very different from focusing on what they're doing wrong, so it might feel awkward for both us and our children. As one parent told us, "When I was growing up, the only time I knew I was doing something right was when I didn't hear from my parents. But I always heard from them when I did something wrong!" Set those awkward feelings aside and get comfortable with letting your children know what they're doing right!

Let's look at some examples of how parents use Effective Praise.

EXAMPLE 1

Your teenager loans his sweat-shirt to his younger sister.

Step 1. Show your approval.
"Hey!" (Enthusiastically, with a pat on the shoulder.)

Step 2. Describe the positive behavior.
"That was nice of you to let your sister borrow your sweatshirt."

Step 3. Give a reason.
"Maybe she'll do something nice for you sometime."

EXAMPLE 2

Mom enters the room to find her two children dusting furniture and folding laundry.

Step 1. Show your approval.
"Kids!" (Pleasantly surprised.)

Step 2. Describe the positive behavior.
"You did a great job remember-ing to do your chores."

Step 3. Give a reason.
"When you get things done early like this, you have more time to do the things you want!"

EXAMPLE 3

Two children have gotten ready for school in the morning without fighting.

Step 1. Show your approval.
Mom pats her son on the shoulder and smiles at her daughter.

Step 2. Describe the positive behavior.
"It's good to see you two getting along in the morning."

Step 3. Give a reason.
"You know if you keep cooperating like this, maybe we won't have to get up so early!"

Steps for Effective Praise

Effective Praise has four steps.

1. Show your approval.
2. Describe the positive behavior.
3. Give a reason.
4. Reward. *(Optional)*

Show your approval.

There are many words that show your satisfaction with your child's behavior. Show a little excitement! Say things such as, "Awesome," "Terrific," " Wow," "You're right on target," "I love you," or "I'm impressed!" Showing your approval is a lot like the general praise described earlier in this chapter. But don't stop there.

Describe the positive behavior.

In this step, describe the specific behaviors your child did well. Make sure your children understand what they did so that they can repeat those behaviors in the future. For example, "Sue, thanks for cleaning the dishes and helping me put the leftovers away." Or, "Eddie, I'm glad you washed your hands after you used the toilet." Remember to use words your children understand. Be brief and to the point.

Give a reason.

Children need to know why it is important for them to use certain behaviors. Giving a reason lets them know how a behavior benefits them or others. "Kid-related" reasons help children understand the relationship between their behavior and what happens to them. If your teenager cleans the family room, explain why that behavior is helpful or how it benefits him or her. For example, you could say, "Since you helped me dust and vacuum the family room, I'll have time to take you over to your friend's house when you want to go. I don't think I would have had time if you hadn't helped."

If your younger child lets another child play with a toy first, you could say, "Sharing your toys with others is helpful because they're more likely to share their toys with you."

Here are some descriptions of children's behaviors and corresponding kid-related reasons that other parents have given:

➤ "It's important to accept criticism from your teacher so he knows that you're taking responsibility for the mistakes on your homework. Now, he'll be more likely to help you with problems in the future. "

➤ "When you get home on time, I'll trust you more and probably will let you go out more often."

➤ "Helping others is a real plus. If you do that on the job, your boss is more likely to give you a raise."

 Reward. *(Optional)*

Occasionally, you may want to add a fourth step to Effective Praise – a reward. When your child has made a big improvement in a certain area, you can reward him or her with a special privilege. Rewards can be large or small. Just be sure the size of the reward fits the behavior you want to encourage.

> **TIP...**
> Effective Praise lets your kids know exactly what they do well.

Effective Praise gives you a quick, effective way to let your kids know exactly what they did so well. The more you use Effective Praise, the more likely it is that your child will do things right to get your attention. Plus, you'll spend less time dealing with talking back, tantrums, and those arguments that take up so much of a parent's time.

Here are some examples of how parents use Effective Praise

EXAMPLE 4

Dad asks his daughter to put away her coloring book and crayons.
Step 1. Show your approval.
"Thanks for ..."

Step 2. Describe the positive behavior.
"... putting those away like I asked, Niosha."

Step 3. Give a reason.
"Now, you'll be able to find your crayons and book a lot easier next time."

EXAMPLE 5

Your teenager asks if he can go to a friend's house.
Step 1. Show your approval.
"Thank you ..."

Step 2. Describe the positive behavior.
"... for asking if you can go to your friend's."

Step 3. Give a reason.
"When you ask me so nicely, I'm more likely to let you go."

EXAMPLE 6

Dad enters the kitchen to find his daughter washing the dishes.
Step 1. Show your approval.
"Hey, thanks ..."

Step 2. Describe the positive behavior.
"... for doing the dishes."

Step 3. Give a reason.
"When you do it right away, you've got more time to do what you want to do."

More examples of how parents use Effective Praise

EXAMPLE 7

Your teenager just called home to tell you where he is.

Step 1. Show your approval.
"Thanks for calling me."

Step 2. Describe the positive behavior.
"I'm really glad that you let me know where you are and why you'll be a little late."

Step 3. Give a reason.
"Calling me shows that I can trust you and I'll be more likely to let you go out with your friends in the future."

EXAMPLE 8

A daughter finished her homework before watching TV.

Step 1. Show your approval.
"Way to go, Emily!"

Step 2. Describe the positive behavior.
"You did your homework before watching TV."

Step 3. Give a reason.
"Now, you won't have to do it late at night."

Step 4. Reward.
"Would you like some popcorn when you watch the movie later?"

Helpful Hints

➤ **Use Effective Praise often.** Use Effective Praise any time your child does well and you want to see that behavior occur again in the future. Children like to hear about things they've done well. They love that positive attention from their parents! When you pay attention to the things your children do well, they'll be more likely to do those things more often.

➤ **Praise small steps in the right direction.** Instead of waiting until your children bring home straight A's on their report cards, praise the small steps that will help them improve their grades along the way. Praise behavior such as bringing school books home, spending more time on homework, or turning in homework assignments on time.

➤ **Be specific.** Save "Good boy" or "Good girl" for your pets. Tell your children exactly what they did well. Be specific and clear about what your children do well and they'll be more likely to repeat those behaviors.

➤ **Link your praise to your child's behavior.** Sometimes, we pay attention to our children when we feel good, and ignore them when things aren't going so well for us. Children quickly learn that "What I do really doesn't matter. What really matters is how Mom (or Dad) is feeling." When this happens, kids get inconsistent and confusing messages about their own behavior. So, make sure you link your praise to your child's behavior, not to the changes in your overall moods or feelings.

➤ **Praise positive behavior, no matter how small.** Sometimes, parents tell us that they can't find anything for which to praise their children. Usually, we find that these parents only praise outstanding achievements or momentous occasions. We ask them to look for little things to praise, too. After parents look closely for small improvements, they begin to notice positive changes in their kids' behavior. In addition, the parents feel they get along better with their kids. This is not coincidence. When you pay attention to the little things your children do well, they generally do well on the big things, too.

➤ **Give praise, even for expected behaviors.** Parents have asked us, "Why should I praise my kids for things they're supposed to do?" We answer them with another question: "Do you like being recognized for the things you do well, regardless of whether you're supposed to do them?" Children, like parents, enjoy hearing about what they do well. Praise helps them build confidence in themselves and their abilities.

➤ **Reserve praise for positive behaviors.** We have had parents tell us that they praise their children often, but it doesn't seem to mean much. These parents tend to tell their children that they're doing well, even when they're not. Or they use praise to stop misbehavior, which only encourages more misbehavior! Or they praise their kids for everything! This praise is not contingent on (or linked to) their children's positive behavior. Praise loses its importance if parents give it all the time, whether or not the child has done anything positive.

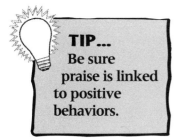

TIP...
Be sure praise is linked to positive behaviors.

➤ **Be sincere and mean what you say.** When you tell your children they're doing something wrong, do you feel like you are just putting on a show? No. But you might feel funny, or even "fake," when you first start pointing out the positive things your children do. Just continue to use praise frequently – and sincerely! In time, you will feel more comfortable praising your kids and they will realize that you do notice when they do something well.

Reaching Goals with Charts and Contracts

The third approach that will help encourage children's positive behavior involves using charts and contracts. Charts and contracts are agreements between you and your kids that spell out what they will receive from you when they behave in certain ways. For example, if you were to write down the agreement, "When you finish cleaning your room, then you can go out and play," you would be making a contract.

You can use charts and contracts:

1. **When you want to help your child change a particular problem behavior.** For example, your daughter may have difficulty getting up and getting ready for school in the morning. You could use a chart or contract to spell out what she could do differently in the morning and what she would get if she gets ready for school on time.

2. **When your child has a goal in mind.** For example, your son may want to work toward earning money for a new bike, having a later bedtime, or being allowed to use the car on weeknights. You could use a chart or contract to keep track of money he saves, the number of nights he goes to bed on time, or how often he brings the car home on time. Then when your son reaches the agreed-upon goals, he earns the privilege of buying the bike, staying up later, or using the car on weeknights.

3. **When you have a particular goal you'd like your child to achieve.** You may want your children to start a savings account, get more involved in school activities, mow the lawn regularly, or keep their rooms clean. A chart or contract can help them keep track of their progress, and give you a clear measure of how they're doing.

TIP...
Use a chart to solve a problem or help your child reach a goal.

There are three steps to charts and contracts:

1. Identify the behavior your child needs to change.

2. Decide what privileges your child can earn.

3. Discuss how long the agreement is in effect.

Charts

| EXAMPLE 1 | *(Please refer to Micah's Morning Routine chart on page 31.)*

Micah, 8, has a hard time getting up and getting ready for school in the morning. Let's look at how a chart can help him with these problem behaviors. *Follow these steps*:

Identify the behavior your child needs to change.

Mom and Micah agree that he needs to get up right away when she wakes him. Next, he needs to get dressed, eat breakfast, brush his teeth, and wash his face.

Decide what privileges your child can earn.

Micah gets stars and "happy faces" on his chart and free time for play in the morning when he gets ready on time.

Discuss how long the agreement is in effect.

Mom and Micah will review the chart every day to keep track of how Micah is doing. They will continue using the chart until Micah consistently gets up on time in the morning.

EXAMPLE 1

Micah's Morning Routine

(Please refer to Example 1 on page 30.)

	Get Dressed	Make Bed	Eat Breakfast	Brush Teeth	Ready for School on Time
Monday					
Tuesday					
Wednesday					
Thursday					
Friday					
Saturday					
Sunday					

Each day that I have 3 stars, I get to pick one of the following:

1. Call a friend on the phone.
2. Ride my bike.
3. Use special glass at dinner.

Each day that I have 4 stars, I get to pick two from this list or the 3-star list.

1. Go to bed 15 minutes later.
2. Call two friends on the phone.
3. Play a card game with Mom or Dad.

Each day that I have 5 stars, I get to pick three things to do from any list.

1. Go to bed 30 minutes later.
2. Have a friend over to play.
3. Go to a friend's house to play.

EXAMPLE 2

Sarah's parents would like to help her read more during the summer. They decide to use a chart to encourage her to read and keep track of her progress. *Follow these steps:*

Identify the behavior your child needs to change.

Mom and Dad would like Sarah to read more so they are asking her to read at least 15 minutes per day. She can read books of her choice as long as they are okay with her mom and dad. They also would like her to read aloud to them on occasion.

Decide what privileges your child can earn.

Sarah can have a friend stay over night at her house after she reads at least 15 minutes for six days. Sarah and her dad also talk about making a list of other privileges for future use.

Discuss how long the agreement is in effect.

The agreement will be in effect for at least six days, but it is likely that the parents will want to continue using the chart throughout the summer to encourage continued reading.

Sarah's Reading Rampage

SUNDAY	MONDAY	TUESDAY	WEDNESDAY	THURSDAY	FRIDAY	SATURDAY
1 ★ *I read 15 minutes.*	2 ✓ *I read 16 minutes.*	3 *Good Job Sarah!* *I read 19 minutes.*	4 ★ *I read 16 minutes.*	5 📖 *I read 15 minutes.*	6 *You did it! Now your friend can stay over!* *I read 17 minutes.*	7
8	9	10	11	12	13	14
14	15	16	17	18	19	20

Identify the Behavior:
The behavior your child needs to change is reading.

Rewarding Privileges:
Sarah can have a friend stay over night at her house after she reads for at least 15 minutes for six days.

Length of Agreement:
The agreement is in effect until Sarah reads on six days.

EXAMPLE 3 *(Please refer to Billy's Bedtime Bonanza chart on page 34.)*

Billy, 10, has a hard time getting to bed on time each night. His parents decide to try a chart to help him. *Follow these steps:*

Identify the behavior your child needs to change.
Billy's parents want him to go to bed on time each night.

Decide what privileges your child can earn.
Billy wants later bedtimes, especially on weekends.

Discuss how long the agreement is in effect.
The parents set up a chart to help Billy get to bed on time. They review the chart every night. Billy can earn later bedtimes on Friday and Saturday nights when he goes to bed on time during the week. Billy's parents can keep this agreement in effect until Billy consistently goes to bed on time without a problem.

Let's look at the details of Billy's chart. Billy's bedtime on weeknights is 9 o'clock. Each weeknight that Billy goes to bed on time without arguing, he draws a stick figure on the chart. The number of times Billy gets to bed on time determines

> **TIP...**
> Charts are useful in helping children attain their goals.

how late he gets to stay up on Friday and Saturday nights. So, going to bed on time without arguing on three of the five weeknights will earn Billy a 9:45 p.m. bedtime on Friday and Saturday. He can extend his weekend bedtime by another half hour by getting to bed on time all five weeknights.

You can use a chart like Billy's Bedtime Bonanza to help your child reach many different goals, such as completing homework, being ready for school on time in the morning, helping others each day, or keeping a bedroom clean.

Parents and children enjoy creating charts together. Young children, in particular, love to get out the crayons and make a colorful chart. This is a positive way to get your child involved in the process and gives you one more thing to praise.

Two additional charts are on the following pages. You may photocopy these charts and use them as is or adapt the charts to more closely fit your child's situation.

EXAMPLE 3

Billy's Bedtime Bonanza

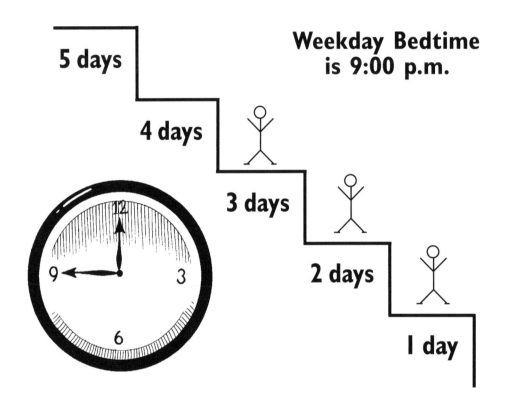

Weekday Bedtime is 9:00 p.m.

5 days

4 days

3 days

2 days

1 day

Each school night that I get to bed on time, I draw a stick figure on my chart. The number of times I get to bed on time tells me how late I can stay up on Friday and Saturday nights.

Friday and Saturday Bedtimes

1 day	9:15 p.m.
2 days	9:30 p.m.
3 days	9:45 p.m.
4 days	10:00 p.m.
5 days	10:30 p.m.

(Please refer to Example 3 on page 33.)

Sammy's S Curve

Each time Mom finds me playing nicely
with my sister, I get to color in a
circle. When three circles are colored,
I get the reward.

Behavior: Playing nicely with my sister.

Reward: Mom reads a book to me.

Reward: Play catch for 15 minutes with Dad.

Reward: Pick a snack.

Reggie's Rebound

Each day that I finish my homework, I get to color a basketball.
On weekends, I get to color a ball if I read for
30 minutes. Each day that I color a ball, I get to shoot
baskets outside with Mom for 15 minutes.

End of the Week Bonus

On Saturday, I get a bonus for having 4 or more balls
colored during the week.

4 balls colored = grocery shopping on Saturday
5 balls colored = friends come over on Saturday
6 balls colored = bike ride on Sunday with Dad
7 balls colored = friends stay overnight on Saturday

Contracts

Here are some examples of contracts parents and children have used to reach goals together. In this first example, Tina, 16, has had trouble getting her homework completed on time. Tina and her mother have gotten into many arguments about her incomplete homework. *Follow these steps:*

 Identify the behavior your child needs to change.
Mom wants to get some rules in place to help Tina consistently complete her homework and to reduce the number of arguments they have about homework.

 Decide what privileges your child can earn.
Tina likes talking with friends on the phone and watching TV.

 Discuss how long the agreement is in effect.
Tina's mother wants her to study in the kitchen for two weeks before they'll decide whether Tina can study in her room. The contract will likely stay in place until Tina consistently hands in her completed assignments and improves her grades.

Here's what the contract might say.

Tina's Homework Agreement

> Tina will study one hour every day, Sunday through Thursday, right after supper until her homework is finished. Tina will study in the kitchen for two weeks. If she does well for those two weeks, she can do her homework in her bedroom. After Tina finishes her homework, she can watch TV or use the phone until ten o'clock.
>
> *Mary Ondar* Tina Ondar

Here's how a contract might work with Greg, a 15-year-old, whose goal is to have a later curfew. Greg's parents want him to consistently come home on time. The contract incorporates both Greg's and his parents' goals.

Identify the behavior your child needs to change.

Greg's parents want him to consistently come home on time.

Decide what privileges your child can earn.

Greg wants a later curfew.

Discuss how long the agreement is in effect.

Greg's parents feel that if he can come home on time for four weeks in a row, they can trust him with a later curfew.

Greg's Curfew Agreement

Greg agrees to be home by 9 o'clock on Sunday through Thursday nights and by 11 o'clock on Friday and Saturday nights. If he does this for four weeks in a row, he gets a later weekend curfew. If Greg is late coming home, he loses going out the following night and his four weeks of coming home on time begin again the next time he goes out.

Mom and Dad agree to let Greg stay out until 11:30 p.m. on Friday and Saturday nights after he comes home on time for four weeks in a row. We will mark the calendar each night after Greg comes home on time. This will continue for four weeks or until the contract is re-negotiated.

Greg Jackson   Peg Jackson
Bill Jackson

Helpful Hints

➤ **State the goal in a positive way.** Use "When you finish your homework, you can watch TV." instead of, "If you don't finish your homework, you can't watch TV." When you word your contract in a positive way, your child is working to reach a goal, rather than to avoid failure.

➤ **Follow through on the agreement.** Be sure to review your child's progress each day. When your child reaches the goal, give your child the privilege she earned. And provide plenty of praise!

➤ **Make the goals specific and measurable.** A goal of "completing homework each night" is easier to measure than "doing better in school." It's easier to tell if your child is "offering to help Mom once a day" than "being more responsible."

➤ **Keep the goals reasonable.** Setting reachable goals is especially important when you are first introducing the idea of a chart or contract. Keep a child's age and ability in mind when helping them set goals. Remember, the goal of using charts and contracts is to help children be successful. Reasonable goals help children gain confidence and increase the likelihood that they'll continue trying to improve in the future.

➤ **Make it fun.** Use charts and contracts to help kids reach goals and experience success. This will be more enjoyable if it's fun for you and your child. Make a big deal out of each day's progress and use lots of praise during the day when your child is working toward the goal.

Summary

The more often we pay attention to the good things our children do, the more time they'll spend doing good things. One way to pay attention is with general praise and affection.

Use Effective Praise to help your children improve specific behaviors. Be sure to link Effective Praise to your children's positive behavior. That's what makes it effective! Parents provide praise and encouragement for very specific things their kids have done. This attention to specific behavior increases the likelihood that these same behaviors will occur again.

Charts and contracts are a great way to help children see the successes they achieve. They also open lines of communication so parents and children reach goals together.

Questions and Comments from Parents

Q. Should I give my children something every time they do something right?

A. If you're asking, "Do I need to give my children toys or treats or special privileges every time they do something right?" the answer is, "No." More often than not, your attention and encouragement may be all that's needed when children do well. In time, children's sense of accomplishment will be enough for them to do what's right. Until then, use praise and positive consequences to increase behaviors that your children don't use routinely. You may have to give this positive attention frequently to help get the behavior started. For behaviors that children use more often or on a regular basis, give praise and use less frequent consequences.

Q. All of this praise stuff is nothing more than a bribe.

A. A bribe is when we reward children for negative behaviors. For example, it's a bribe when a young child is whining for candy at the store, and you give him the candy to get him to be quiet. He just learned that whining in the store pays off and he'll be more likely to whine in the store in the future. On the other hand, Effective Praise is a reward for doing things well. So, if your child helps out in the store and stays by your side without pestering you to buy things, use Effective Praise to let her know she's done well! That's good teaching, not a bribe.

Q. My son is finally starting to come in on time at night. How long am I going to have to praise him for it?

A. Praise him until coming home on time becomes routine or a habit for him. When he comes home on time consistently, you may praise him less often, but don't stop praising him completely.

Q. When my daughter does something right, I tell her about it, but it doesn't seem to change anything.

A. You may need to change how you show your approval. Be more specific, use a different reason, or use a positive consequence to get things "jump started." Praising children helps build positive relationships and positive relationships often lead to improved behavior, but it takes time. So, keep praising and don't give up. You also will want to use the other Common Sense Parenting skills in this book to help improve your child's behavior.

Q. My child already goes to bed on time. Why should I praise him for it?

A. That's great that he already goes to bed on time. But remember that praising him lets him know he is doing just what you want. You may not need to praise him every time he goes to bed on time, but the occasional praise will help him understand that you appreciate what he does.

Q. My daughter doesn't do anything I think she should be praised for.

A. Parenting is one of the most challenging and potentially frustrating things any of us will ever do. It may seem difficult at times, but try to look for little things, routine things, or positive attempts at new things that your daughter does and praise small steps in the right direction. It might take a lot of effort to help her start behaving in more positive ways, but the effort will be worth it in the long run.

Q. **My kid doesn't like to be praised!**

A. Many of us feel uncomfortable either giving or receiving praise. Practice using praise frequently and, over time, you're likely to feel more comfortable giving praise and your kids may feel more comfortable getting praise. When kids get older, some of them don't like being praised in public, especially in front of friends. In those cases, save your praise for times when you're alone with your kids.

Q. **Do I always have to give a "kid" reason?**

A. Kid-related reasons make it easier for your child to understand how the behavior benefits him or her. Use kid reasons whenever you can, especially when your child is first learning or demonstrating a new behavior. But parents also want to give children "other-oriented" reasons, such as "Thanks for helping me clean the house. Now it looks great and it will give my friends from work a good impression of our family when they come over tonight." These other-oriented reasons help expand a child's understanding of how their actions help others, too.

Exercise 1 – Identifying Positive Behavior

Write examples of things your children do well.

Child's Name_____

1. _____

   _____

2. _____

   _____

3. _____

   _____

4. _____

   _____

Child's Name_____

1. _____

   _____

2. _____

   _____

3. _____

   _____

4. _____

   _____

Child's Name_____

1. _____

   _____

2. _____

   _____

3. _____

   _____

4. _____

   _____

Child's Name_____

1. _____

   _____

2. _____

   _____

3. _____

   _____

4. _____

   _____

Exercise 2 – Practice Using Effective Praise

Watch the children in each video scene. On this and the following pages, write how you would use Effective Praise if these were your children. Then compare your answer with the answers parents give in class. Each of us is unique so your answer is likely to be somewhat different from the parents in class. When comparing your answer, don't judge yourself on whether your words matched identically. Instead, check to see if you were specific with your descriptions of what the children did well and whether you provided a reason that was kid-related.

Scene 1

Daughter avoids a fight with her brother over the bathroom.

1. Show approval. _____

   _____

2. Describe the positive behavior. _____

   _____

   _____

3. Give a reason. _____

   _____

4. Reward. *(Optional)* _____

   _____

Scene 2

Son comes home rather than drinking with friends.

1. Show approval. _____

   _____

2. Describe the positive behavior. _____

   _____

   _____

3. Give a reason. _____

   _____

4. Reward. *(Optional)* _____

   _____

Scene 3

Daughter calls home rather than going to her friend's house when her friend's parents aren't home.

1. Show approval. _____

   _____

2. Describe the positive behavior. _____

   _____

   _____

3. Give a reason. _____

   _____

4. Reward. *(Optional)* _____

   _____

Scene 4

Daughter calls a friend to get homework assignment.

1. Show approval. _____

   _____

2. Describe the positive behavior. _____

   _____

   _____

3. Give a reason. _____

   _____

4. Reward. *(Optional)* _____

   _____

Homework 1 – Effective Praise

Use Effective Praise frequently with your child. Over the next week, record how you used the steps of Effective Praise in three situations.

Behavior: _____

1. Show approval. _____

    _____

2. Describe the positive behavior. _____

    _____

3. Give a reason. _____

    _____

4. Reward. *(Optional)* _____

    _____

Behavior: _____

1. Show approval. _____

    _____

2. Describe the positive behavior. _____

    _____

3. Give a reason. _____

    _____

4. Reward. *(Optional)* _____

    _____

Behavior: _____

1. Show approval. _____

    _____

2. Describe the positive behavior. _____

    _____

3. Give a reason. _____

    _____

4. Reward. *(Optional)* _____

    _____

CHAPTER 3

Preventing Misbehavior

> **In this chapter, we'll be learning:**
> - ➤ **How parents can prevent child behavior problems by using "Preventive Teaching"**
> - ➤ **How to teach social skills to children**

Parents often tell us that they feel like police, always correcting their kids' problems. These days, police forces have moved into the prevention arena to try to keep problems from happening. Parents can take this approach, too.

Ben Franklin once said that an ounce of prevention is worth a pound of cure. As parents, you can save yourself time and frustration when you work to set your children up for success by letting them know what to do *before* they need to do it. We call this skill Preventive Teaching.

Preventive Teaching

Preventive Teaching is teaching your child what he or she will need to know for a future situation and practicing it in advance. Preventive Teaching lets your child know what you expect, *before* the situation occurs.

ACTIVITY 1

Preventive Teaching

On the following lines, write examples of new situations your children might be facing in the near future. Then, use Preventive Teaching BEFORE your children are in those new situations, so they'll be more successful at the time.

1 _____

_____

_____

_____

2 _____

_____

_____

_____

3 _____

_____

_____

_____

When to Use Preventive Teaching

There are two types of situations in which you can use Preventive Teaching:

➤ When your child is learning something new.

➤ When your child is facing a situation that has been a problem in the past.

In each case, use Preventive Teaching before your child faces a new situation or before potential problems. For example, if your daughter frequently argues when you ask her to hang up the phone, you can use Preventive Teaching before she calls her friends. This way she can practice how to answer you correctly when you let her know her telephone time is up. It's best to use Preventive Teaching when your child is calm and attentive, not after a misbehavior or when he or she is upset.

> **TIP...**
> Use Preventive Teaching before your child faces a new situation in their life.

Before new situations

Preventive Teaching is a simple concept, but most parents don't use it as often as they could. Here are some examples of how parents have used Preventive Teaching before situations that were new to their children.

➤ "I used Preventive Teaching before tryouts at the beginning of the basketball season so that my child would know how to respond to coaches' instructions."

➤ "When my son got in a fight, I used Preventive Teaching to show him how to apologize to the other kid. Apologizing was new for him."

➤ "My daughter had to make a presentation to classmates. I used Preventive Teaching before the presentation so that she wasn't so nervous."

➤ "When my son fell behind in his assignments, I taught him how to ask for make-up work in school."

➤ "My daughter just got her learner's permit to drive. I used Preventive Teaching to help her learn how to back the car out of a parking space without hitting the cars around her."

Before situations that have resulted in past problems

Here are some examples of times where parents have used Preventive Teaching to help their children be successful – instead of repeating past problems. These parents used Preventive Teaching before their children were in situations in which the children had had behavior problems.

➤ "Before my older kids go out with friends, I use Preventive Teaching to remind them how to get home on time."

➤ "Before they go to school in the morning, I talk to them about how to get their homework done as soon as they come home."

➤ "Before my kids go out with friends, I teach them how to say 'No' if their friends pressure them to drink or do other things that are wrong."

➤ "Before they go out to play, I teach them how to come in when I call them."

➤ "Before taking them to the store, I teach them how to stand quietly and not ask for candy in the checkout lane."

➤ "Before I tell them that they can't go to a friend's house or watch TV, I use Preventive Teaching to teach them how to accept 'No' for an answer."

➤ "They have had problems doing what I tell them, so I teach them how to follow directions when I ask them to help around the house."

(Be sure to complete Activity 2 on the next page.)

ACTIVITY 2

On the following lines, write examples of past child behavior problems where using Preventive Teaching would be helpful.

 1. _____

_____

_____

_____

 2. _____

_____

_____

_____

 3. _____

_____

_____

_____

Steps for Preventive Teaching

Preventive Teaching has three steps:

1. Describe what you would like.
2. Give a reason.
3. Practice.

Let's look at the steps and see why each is important.

Describe what you would like.

Before your children can do what you want, they must first know what it is you expect. Be specific when you describe your expectations. Make sure your children understand.

Give a reason.

Reasons explain to a child how new skills and appropriate behaviors are helpful and how inappropriate behaviors are harmful. The best reasons are those that relate directly to your child's life. Simply telling your kids, "Pick up your room because I said so," is a command, not a reason. It does not show your kids any relationship between their actions and future benefits to them. Instead, you might say something such as, "Pick up your room so that no one will step on your toys and break them." Kid-related reasons help make it clearer to children how they will benefit from doing what you teach them.

> **TIP...**
> Reasons show a relationship between an action and the future benefit of that action.

Practice.

Knowing what to do and being able to do it are two different things. Any new skill needs practice. You can tell your son how to ride a bicycle, but that will not ensure that he could hop right on and start riding. He needs practice before he'll be able to ride well. Likewise, you can tell your daughter how to get away from the class bully, but she'll be more likely to be successful if she's had a chance to practice what she should do and say in that situation. It takes practice to become good at almost anything.

Let's look at the steps of Preventive Teaching in some examples.

 EXAMPLE 1

Anthony, 15, has trouble getting ready for school on time in the morning. His mother uses Preventive Teaching to help him get into the habit of getting prepared for school the night before so he'll be ready on time in the morning.

 Describe what you would like.

Mom: "Anthony, come here. I want to talk with you…Look, you've been late for school almost every day this week."

Anthony: "But Mom …"

Mom: "You're not in trouble, so relax. I just want to talk with you about what you can do in the morning to be on time."

Anthony: "Do we have to?"

Mom: "Yes, we have to. Now, after you get through with your homework, all you have to do is get the stuff that you need for school next to the door."

Anthony: "Every night?"

Mom: "Yes, every night."

 Give a reason.

Mom: "Then you'll be more organized in the morning. You'll get to spend more time with your friends before school and you won't be running around here looking for things."

Anthony: "All right."

Practice.

Mom: "Now I want you to go get the stuff you need for school and bring it here so I can see it. Okay?"

Anthony: "Okay." *(Anthony goes and gets his schoolbooks and bag and brings them back to his mother.)*

Mom: "Okay, it looks like you have everything here. Now, you just need to put it next to the front door and you'll be ready to go in the morning. Okay?"

Anthony: "Okay."

EXAMPLE 2

Mom is going to the store with her two children. In the past, the kids have whined and complained when she's told them that they can't have candy or other things they ask for. Before going to the store, Mom is going to use Preventive Teaching to teach them what they should do when she says "No" at the store.

TIP...
Preventive Teaching doesn't guarantee success, but makes it more likely.

1 **Describe what you would like.**

Mom: "Melita, Peter, hurry up. Let's go. When we get to the store, I want you to stay with me. If you ask me for something, and I say 'No,' just say 'Okay' and don't argue."

2 **Give a reason.**

Mom: "That way we'll get home quicker and you'll have more time to play."

Peter: "Yeah, Mom."

Mom: "How about you, Melita?"

Melita: "Oh, okay."

3 **Practice.**

Mom: "Peter, ask me to buy you something."

Peter: "Mom, can I have a candy bar?"

Mom: "Good. I'd probably say 'No,' it's too close to dinner time. So, then what would you say, Melita?"

Melita: "All right, Mom."

Mom: "How about you, Peter?"

Peter: "Okay."

Mom: "All right, let's try and remember that when we go shopping this time."

EXAMPLE 3

In the past, when Micah asks to go somewhere and his mom says, "No" he has had tantrums and argued with her. So, at a neutral time – when there isn't a problem – Mom should use Preventive Teaching to help Micah learn how to accept "No" from her. Here's how she might teach him.

 Describe what you would like.

Mom: "Micah, I know sometimes when you ask me to do something and I say 'No,' it's hard for you. You start arguing with me and end up in more trouble. Right?"

Micah: "Yeah."

Mom: "When I tell you 'No' I want you to look at me, without arguing and say, 'Okay.' Okay?"

Micah: "Okay."

 Give a reason.

Mom: "If you can do that, I'm more likely to listen to you and you won't end up in trouble."

 Practice.

Mom: "Let's say you ask me to go to a friend's house and I say 'No.' What would you say?"

Micah: "Okay. But Mom why can't I go?"

Mom: "Then I'd probably say, 'It's a school night, Micah.' What would you say then?"

Micah: "All right."

Mom: "Good. You've accepted my answer and you calmly asked for a reason."

Activity 3

When do I use Preventive Teaching?

Micah, 8, wants to go to his friend's house. He comes into the kitchen and asks his mom if he can go. When his mom says "No," Micah starts yelling and arguing. Mom starts using Preventive Teaching to teach Micah how to accept "No" for an answer. Why is this the wrong time to use Preventive Teaching?

_____

_____

_____

_____

_____

_____

_____

_____

(Answer: Use Preventive Teaching BEFORE a problem occurs, when a child is calm – not after the problem when the child is upset. [If a problem is already occurring, then Mom can use a skill we call Corrective Teaching, which will be discussed in the next chapter.])

In these first three examples, parents used Preventive Teaching to teach children what they can do to avoid past problems. In this next example, a mother will use Preventive Teaching to help her children be successful in a new situation.

EXAMPLE 4

Mom is starting a new bedtime routine with her two children. Before she puts the new routine into effect, Mom will use Preventive Teaching to help her children understand what she expects from them. Here's how it might sound.

 Describe what you would like.

Mom: "We're going to try something a little bit different tonight. What I want you to do at 8 o'clock is brush your teeth, put your pajamas on, and at 8:30, lights should be out and you both should be in bed."

Alisha: "That doesn't sound much like fun."

 Give a reason.

Mom: "Well, if you get done really quickly, Alisha, you can listen to your music and maybe read your comics, and maybe I will read Niosha a story. Would you like that?"

Niosha: "Yeah."

 Practice.

Mom: "Why don't you both finish your cookies and then, I want you, Alisha, to get your pajamas on and you, Niosha, to brush your teeth. Okay?"

Kids: "Okay."

Helpful Hints

Practice makes... not perfect, but it will help your children behave better. So, include practice whenever you want to help your child improve behavior. Children occasionally are reluctant to practice. But practice actually eases embarrassment and raises kids' self-confidence. Provide encouragement when they practice and praise them a lot for trying to do things well.

➤ **Practice with young children.** When practicing with younger children, try to make practice fun, yet realistic. Young children like to pretend and play different roles in the practices.

➤ **Practice with teens.** Older children and adolescents can be more of a challenge when it comes to practicing. Set up the practice with words like, "Show me how you would handle..." or "Okay, tell me what you would say to... ." This gives older children an opportunity to demonstrate their ability without feeling like you are talking down to them.

➤ **Remember that it takes time to change and learn.** Don't expect perfection the first time you practice. The speed with which your children improve their behavior depends on how often you practice, how well you practice, how consistently you pay attention to the correct behavior when it occurs, and how consistently you correct the problem behavior when it occurs. Change takes time.

➤ **Use Preventive Teaching to practice more than one possible outcome.** If you are practicing a complex skill or a difficult situation (such as how to say "No" to a friend who is trying to get you to drink alcohol) try to cover several different outcomes. Emphasize to your child that he or she is practicing possible ways to handle a situation and the outcome won't always be the same as the one you practice. You cannot guarantee your children's success in every situation. But using Preventive Teaching increases the likelihood that they'll be prepared for most situations.

➤ **Use prompts to remind your child what to do.** After using Preventive Teaching several times to teach a skill, you may only need to provide a reminder – a preventive prompt. For example, let's say that you and your daughter have practiced how to stay calm when she gets upset with her friends. Before she goes out to play, you could say, "Remember, Sharon, stay calm just like we practiced. When you're upset, don't say anything mean to your friends. Just take a few deep breaths and walk away from them if you have to."

Teaching Children Social Skills

So far we've talked about *how* (with Preventive Teaching) to help kids be successful by teaching them what they need to know, before they need to know it. Now, we're going to discuss *what* to teach children. The "what" we'll be learning about is social skills.

TIP... Use Preventive Teaching to teach social skills.

Social skills are sets of specific behaviors, linked together in a certain order, that help us get along with other people and make appropriate decisions in social situations.

Think a minute about what you do (your behavior) when you meet someone for the first time. You probably: 1) stand up straight, 2) look at the person, 3) smile, 4) give a firm handshake, and 5) say your name and something like, "It's nice to meet you." This is an example of how these five behaviors fit together to make up the social skill of how to introduce yourself.

On the following pages are additional examples of social skills and how parents have used Preventive Teaching to teach the skills to their children. The behaviors listed for each social skill are guidelines. Adapt each social skill to fit your expectations for your children. Additional social skills are in Appendix B.

EXAMPLE 1

Dad and his daughter, Sarah, are in the kitchen making oatmeal. Dad decides that this is a good opportunity to use Preventive Teaching to teach Sarah the social skill, "How to follow instructions."

How to follow instructions

1. Look at the person.
2. Say "Okay."
3. Do what is asked.
4. Check back to let the person know you are finished.

 Describe what you would like.

Sarah:	"Can I stir the oatmeal?"
Dad:	"Go right ahead. Just don't slop it out. Okay?"
Sarah:	"Okay."
Dad:	"You know Sarah, this is a good example of following directions. Because if we put the oatmeal in and didn't put the water in, we'd just have a big mess, wouldn't we?"
Sarah:	"Yeah, and it would taste yucky!"
Dad:	"It's like that when Mom and I tell you what to do around the house. When we say pick up your room, brush your teeth, turn off the TV ..."
Sarah:	"... or set the table."
Dad:	"Right. Now what I want you to do when we tell you to do something around the house is look at us and say, 'Okay.' Then go do it. All right?"
Sarah:	"Uh huh."

Give a reason.

Dad: "That way you're not spending all this time arguing and then you've got more time to do what you want to do."

Sarah: "Yeah, but sometimes I'm busy."

Dad: "Right. Everybody's busy sometimes, and we'll try to be considerate of that. But if we tell you to go do something now, it's important that you go do it right now. Okay?"

Sarah: "Okay."

Practice.

Dad: "Now, I'm going to tell you to do something, and I want you to look at me, say, 'Okay,' and go do it. Okay?"

Sarah: "Uh huh."

Dad: "Sarah, please go put the oatmeal away."

Sarah: "Okay." *(Sarah puts the outmeal in the cabinet.)*

Dad: "There, see, that was easy. It took a second, and I want you to do this every time we tell you what to do. Okay?"

Sarah: "Okay."

We want to teach our children social skills that they can use in many different situations. In this example with Sarah, she learned how to follow directions or instructions in the kitchen. What she learned can carry over to many other situations and locations. For example, she will be asked to follow directions from her parents, or at school when a teacher gives instructions, or on numerous other occasions in church, at the store, or at a friend's house. Sarah's ability to follow instructions will help her be successful in almost every area of her life, so teaching her this skill is a great help to her.

Here are some additional examples of how parents use Preventive Teaching to teach social skills to their children.

> ### EXAMPLE 2

In this example, Brooke is going to the store with her friends. In the past her friends have shoplifted items and gotten in trouble. Mom wants to make sure Brooke knows what to say and do if her friends try to pressure her into stealing the next time she's at the store with them. She uses Preventive Teaching to teach Brooke how to say "No" to friends. This social skill has four steps:

How to say "No" to friends

1. Say "No" and state your reason clearly.

2. Be persistent with your "No" answer.

3. Ask the person to leave you alone.

4. Remove yourself from the situation, if necessary.

In this conversation, Mom teaches all four steps for saying "No" to friends. She slightly adapts the steps, but, for the most part, they're all there. Here's how it might go in this situation with Brooke.

Describe what you would like.

Mom: "Brooke, can I talk to you before you start listening to your music?"

Brooke: "Sure, Mom. What's up?"

Mom: "I want to talk with you about something that came up awhile back. You're going to the store with your friends today and I'd like to know what you're going to say if one of your friends tries to get you to take something without paying for it."

Brooke: "Mom, you know I wouldn't steal anything."

Mom: "I know. But sometimes it's hard to say 'No' to your friends."

Practice.

Mom: "What would you say if they kept on you and they said, 'Put the makeup in your pocket, nobody's going to see you, just take it.'"

Brooke: "I'd say, 'I'm not doing it.'"

Mom: "I know. But what if they kept saying something like, 'Don't you want it? Don't be such a chicken. It's easy.'"

Brooke: "I'd still say, 'Sure, I want it, but not that bad. I'm not going to take it.'"

> *Mom:* "You can also remember to say things like, 'My parents would kill me. My dad would cut off my fingers and I couldn't wear the nail polish any way.'"
>
> *Brooke:* "Yeah, like they'd really believe that."

 Give a reason.

> *Mom:* "It's not so much about them believing you. You just want them to leave you alone. Then, you can call me, and I'll come pick you up when there's problems like that."
>
> *Brooke:* "Okay."
>
> *Mom:* "Remember to do that when you're with your friends and they're trying to get you to do something you know is wrong! Okay?"
>
> *Brooke:* "Okay."

EXAMPLE 3

In this next example, Brandon, 15, often argues and talks back when he gets an answer that he doesn't like from his dad. Dad is using Preventive Teaching to teach Brandon the social skill of how to accept "No" answers. Here are the steps to accepting "No" answers.

How to accept "No" answers

1. Look at the person.

2. Say "Okay."

3. Calmly ask for a reason if you really don't understand.

4. If you disagree, ask to bring it up later.

In the following conversation, Brandon's father adapts these four steps to fit his expectations for his son. Brandon's father only wants Brandon to use step two, "Say, 'Okay.'" He's not interested in the other three steps at this time. Brandon's father has picked the step that means the most to him, and looks like it will be the most help to his son. Later, Brandon's father may want to teach additional steps, but for now, step two is the only one he is emphasizing.

 Describe what you would like.

> *Dad:* "Rain all day! There goes your baseball practice."
>
> *Brandon:* "Yeah. I wonder if they're going to cancel the game tomorrow."
>
> *Dad:* "I don't know. I guess we're going to have to wait and see. You know sometimes, we can't always get what we want and we're going to be a little disappointed."
>
> *Brandon:* "Yeah, that happens a lot to me."

Give a reason.

Dad: ""I know sometimes if I say 'No' to you, you're going to be disappointed. But on those times when you can just say 'Okay' I'm going to be really proud of the way you handled that and, next time, I'm going to want to try to say, 'Yes' whenever I can. Does that make sense to you?"

Brandon: "So you mean, you don't want me to argue with you when you tell me, 'No.'"

Dad: "That's exactly it."

Brandon: "Yeah, I know."

Practice.

Dad: "Great! How about, let's say, you want to buy a new glove, and I have to tell you 'No.' What are you going to say?"

Brandon: "I'm just going to say, 'Okay.'"

Dad: "Perfect. Wonderful."

EXAMPLE 4

In this fourth example, a father uses Preventive Teaching to teach his daughter how to ask permission. He uses all four steps but adapts the skill to fit the situation with his daughter.

How to ask permission

1. Look at the person.
2. Ask rather than demand.
3. Give a reason for what you want to do.
4. Accept the decision.

Describe what you would like.

Dad: "I'm real happy that you came and asked me to use the tools. You know, I want you to remember that whenever you want to use something that belongs to somebody else, you have to ask permission. Right?"

Jennifer: "Yeah."

Dad: "You go to the person, and ask nicely, you don't demand. And you give your reason for wanting to use it. Right?"

Jennifer: "Right."

Practice.

Dad: "Okay, let's say that you want to use the tools to make another birdhouse. What are you going to do?"

Jennifer: "Come and ask you first."

Dad: "Okay. And what are you going to say?"

Jennifer: "Can I use your tools to make another birdhouse?"

Dad: "Okay, good, that's nice. See you asked nicely and you gave a reason. But what if I said, 'No, I'm sorry. I don't want you to make a birdhouse by yourself.' Now, if I do that, you've got to accept my decision. Right?"

Jennifer: "Right."

Dad: "What are you going to say?"

Jennifer: "Would you help me make another one then?"

Dad: "Okay! Good, see. That's nice."

 Give a reason.

Dad: "You asked nicely and I'm probably going to be more likely to help you. Now what do you have left to do?"

What other skills would you like your children to learn? List some of these skills on the lines below.

1. _____

_____

2. _____

_____

3. _____

_____

4. _____

_____

5. _____

_____

6. _____

_____

Parents can teach other social skills at home that will help their children in many social situations. Here are some other skills. (Detailed descriptions of these skills are in Appendix B.)

➤ How to apologize

➤ How to disagree appropriately

➤ How to stay calm

➤ How to accept a consequence

➤ How to accept criticism

➤ How to get along with others

➤ How to let parents know where you are going

Helpful Hints

➤ **Take time to explain to your children when they can use these social skills and why these skills will help them.**

➤ **Help your children understand how one skill can be used in several different situations.** For example, learning how to follow instructions at home is very similar to following instructions at school, on the job, or in athletics.

➤ **Make learning fun.** Praise your kids or reward them with something special for taking the time to learn new social skills.

➤ **Be patient.** After your kids learn a new skill, it may take awhile before they are comfortable using it – before it really becomes a part of them. Learning new skills is an ongoing process.

Summary

Preventive Teaching is a valuable tool for both you and your children. It can increase your children's self-confidence by showing them that they can learn how to change their behaviors and be successful. And, perhaps most importantly, Preventive Teaching allows you and your child to work together toward positive goals.

Social skills give your children a solid foundation for getting along with others and being more successful in many areas of their lives. Children of all ages can benefit from learning social skills. It's just as important for small children to learn how to follow instructions and give compliments as it is for older children and teens. Now is the time to begin teaching your child social skills.

Questions and Comments from Parents

Q. My kid is 16 years old and she will think practicing is stupid.

A. We hear this a lot. One way to practice with teens is to ask them to show you what they would do in that situation. Or ask her how she would handle it. She may still be reluctant to say what she would do, but stick with it. If you can make the practice part of the ongoing conversation, then she'll be much more likely to show you how she would respond in the situation.

Q. What if I use Preventive Teaching and my kid still misbehaves?

A. Preventive Teaching doesn't guarantee that a child's behavior will change. You will likely need to use Preventive Teaching many times before you see results. Nevertheless, each time you use Preventive Teaching, you are increasing the likelihood that your child will get it right the next time. Patience is important. Often, parents are trying to undo several years of problem behaviors. It's not easy to change those behavior patterns so quickly.

In the next chapter, we'll be discussing Corrective Teaching, an effective way of responding to misbehavior. Until then, keep using Preventive Teaching, Effective Praise, and positive and negative consequences.

Q. Can I use Preventive Teaching to teach my children not to use drugs?

A. Sure. Teach them clearly what to say or do in those situations, then have them practice those responses. Also, have them practice how to recognize and avoid those situations. Have them practice responding to different types of attempts by anyone trying to get them to use drugs. *(If you are concerned that your children may be involved with drugs, contact a drug treatment program in your community or call the Boys Town National Hotline at 1-800-448-3000. Counselors are available to help you 24 hours a day, 7 days each week.)*

Q. We just used Preventive Teaching the other day before going out to eat and my child was still awful.

A. You may need to practice more frequently before the actual situation and let your child know what positive and negative consequences are in place. Then consistently follow through with the consequences and any additional teaching. Preventive Teaching does not guarantee positive behavior, but it does make it more likely.

Q. I told my children exactly what they're to do when we left for class tonight, and I know they aren't going to do it. How can I make them?

A. You can't make them, but you can encourage them to make good decisions by using Effective Praise, Preventive Teaching, Corrective Teaching, and consequences. You will learn more about Corrective Teaching and other effective ways of responding to misbehavior in the upcoming chapters.

Q. My children come home late every night, even though I tell them to be in by 9:30. They don't care if I use a consequence.

A. You may need to change the consequence. Make sure it is an effective consequence, and follow through with it. Also, look at size, importance, immediacy, and how consistently you link the consequence to coming home on time. You may also need to use Preventive Teaching to teach them how to get home on time and how to call when they're going to be late. As mentioned in response to some of the other questions, Corrective Teaching also will be helpful when responding to problems such as this.

Exercise 1 – Identifying Social Skills

 Watch the scenes that show parents using Preventive Teaching to teach their children social skills. Then pause the video and match the scene from the left column with the appropriate social skill in the right column.

Scene

_____ 1. Mother and son discussing son's school bus problems.

_____ 2. Father and son discussing son's basketball coach.

_____ 3. Father and daughter discussing how she reacts when she is upset.

_____ 4. Mother and daughter talking about not being able to watch TV after homework.

Social Skills

A. How to stay calm.

B. How to follow instructions.

C. How to ask permission.

D. How to accept a consequence.

E. How to get along with others.

F. How to apologize.

G. How to disagree appropriately.

(Answers: 1-F, 2-G, 3-A, 4-D)

Homework 1 – Preventive Teaching

Write the name of a social skill you would like to teach your child and the specific behavior steps of that skill.

Social Skill: _____

Steps: _____
_____
_____
_____

Use Preventive Teaching frequently to teach social skills to your child. Record how you use the steps of Preventive Teaching in three situations.

Situation:_____

1. Describe what you would like._____
_____

2. Give a reason._____
_____

3. Practice. _____
_____

Situation:_____

1. Describe what you would like._____
_____

2. Give a reason._____
_____

3. Practice. _____
_____

Situation:_____

1. Describe what you would like._____
_____

2. Give a reason._____
_____

3. Practice. _____
_____

CHAPTER 4

Correcting Problem Behaviors

Many parents are looking for a constructive, effective way to respond to children's frequent misbehavior. In this chapter we'll be learning about:

➤ A four-step process called "Corrective Teaching"

➤ Teaching positive social skills as alternatives to problem behaviors

Corrective Teaching

Corrective Teaching involves stopping the problem behavior and teaching your children what they should do differently. The "corrective" part combines clear messages with consequences to help parents stop child behavior problems such as arguing, fighting, yelling, and talking back. The "teaching" part combines teaching and having children practice what they can do instead of using the problem behavior. Corrective Teaching increases the likelihood that children will be successful when they face a similar situation in the future.

As one parent put it, "Corrective Teaching gives me a plan for responding to my kids' misbehavior. I was doing some of it sometimes – like giving consequences – but I really wasn't teaching. So my kids never learned what to do. They only learned what I didn't like."

ACTIVITY 1

What do your kids do that gives you a knot in your stomach?

On the lines below, write down five of your children's problem behaviors that you would like to change. The next time these behaviors occur, you can use Corrective Teaching.

1. _____

   _____

2. _____

   _____

3. _____

   _____

4. _____

   _____

5. _____

   _____

When to Use Corrective Teaching

Use Corrective Teaching any time your kids misbehave; for example, when they ignore you, complain, fight with a brother or sister, or do something else they shouldn't be doing. Here are some specific situations where parents have used Corrective Teaching:

➤ When my kids say I don't do anything for them.

➤ When my kids complain because I ask them to do something around the home.

➤ When my kids are mean to each other. (My older children yell at the younger children or demand that the younger ones do what they're told.)

➤ When my youngest runs around the house yelling and bothering everyone.

➤ When my 10-year-old whines, argues, and fights when I tell him "No."

➤ When my child lies to me. (He tells me that he's been at school all day when I know he's skipped several classes.)

➤ When my kids don't follow my instructions. (I ask them to do their homework and they ignore me and continue to watch TV.)

➤ When my kids argue with my decisions. (They complain if I tell them they can't go out and play with friends.)

➤ When they refuse to accept my criticism or suggestions. (They argue when I ask them to change their clothes for church.)

➤ When my kids don't let me know where they are going or where they've been. (They leave the house without permission.)

➤ When my teens don't follow family rules. (They come home after their curfew or don't call when they're going to be late.)

As a rule, use Corrective Teaching when you see something you want to correct in your children's behavior.

Steps for Corrective Teaching

There are four steps to Corrective Teaching:

1. Stop the problem behavior.
2. Give a consequence.
3. Describe what you want.
4. Practice what you want.

Here's a brief overview of the Corrective Teaching steps.

 Stop the problem behavior.

Stopping the problem behavior helps focus your children's attention on what you are saying. Start by calmly getting their attention and giving them clear instructions, such as, "Stop fighting and sit down in the chair." Eliminate as many distractions as possible and get at their eye level. You want them to concentrate on you and your teaching.

Stop the problem behavior when it's a minor misbehavior. The longer you let the misbehavior continue or the more serious the problem becomes, the more difficult it will be to stop. For example, if your two children are arguing over the TV remote control, ask them to stop arguing right away and continue with the next three steps of Corrective Teaching. If you let them continue arguing, it is likely that the problem will get worse and you will be breaking up a wrestling match rather than an argument.

If the problem behavior has already stopped or occurred earlier, then just describe that behavior. For example, "Danny, before I left for the store, I asked you to pick up your clothes and put away the clean dishes. Instead, you have been playing video games."

 Give a consequence.

Consequences help children make the connection between what they do and what happens as a result of their actions. Remember to use the smallest consequence that will work. If you are having trouble choosing consequences, return to Chapter 1 and read the section on consequences again. Also, be sure to complete the exercises in that chapter that help you pick out consequences that will work best with your children.

If you want Danny to spend less time playing video games and more time following instructions, you would give him a negative consequence. You might say something like, "Since you didn't do what I asked, I want you to fold a load of laundry after you finish the chores I asked you to do earlier. All this has to be done before you play video games again."

> **TIP...**
> Use the smallest consequence that will work.

 Describe what you want.

Be clear and specific, and stick to describing the behavior you want your children to use in place of the problem behavior. Use the social skills described in Chapter 3 to help you identify what you want your kids to do.

In our example, Danny didn't follow his mom's instructions to do a couple of chores. His mom might say, "Okay, Danny, anytime I ask you to do something, I want you to tell me that you'll do it and get started on it right away."

 Practice what you want.

Practice. Practice. Practice. Each time your children practice doing things right, you are increasing their chances for success. Practice lets you know that they understand what you taught them. It also helps them remember what they can do to avoid problems in the future. For example, Mom might say, "Danny, show me how you'll get the chores done next time. "And Danny might slowly answer, "All right," and shuffle off to get started on his chores. Mom says, "Thanks for getting started right away. You just practiced how to follow instructions. Now, you'll get finished sooner and get back to your games."

Corrective Teaching Examples

EXAMPLE 1

Dad is busy repairing the lawnmower. His son comes running out of the house and asks his father to give him a ride to a friend's house. Dad tells his son that he's got to stick with the repair job until it's finished. The son complains and questions why the lawnmower repair can't wait; he wants a ride to his friend's house now. Dad stops repairing the mower and uses Corrective Teaching to teach his son how to accept his answer.

 Stop the problem behavior.

> *Dad:* "Look, Brandon, you made your plans ahead of time without telling me and you're arguing with me now."

 Give a consequence.

> *Dad:* "For that, you can skip going to Brian's altogether."
> *Brandon:* "Whatever."

 Describe what you want.

> *Dad:* "I know you don't like that. But next time, instead of arguing, just say, 'Okay, Dad.' Give me a nice answer and we'll see what happens. Maybe next time I'll say 'Yes.'"
> *Brandon:* "Okay."

 Practice what you want.

> *Dad:* "So, show me what you're going to say the next time I tell you, 'No, you can't go to Brian's.'"
> *Brandon:* (Reluctantly) "Okay. But can I go after dinner?"
> *Dad:* "No. But maybe in the future you can, if you keep answering me like that."
> *Brandon:* "All right."

In this example, Dad is teaching his son to use the skill, "How to accept my answer," as an alternative to arguing. For this father, the skill has one step: Say "Okay" in a nice voice tone. Some parents may expect more from their children. For example, your expectations for accepting an answer might be: 1) Look at me; 2)Use a pleasant voice and say "Okay;" and 3)Ask questions if you really don't understand.

What you expect from your children in this type of situation is up to you. Be clear when you communicate those expectations to your children.

EXAMPLE 2

Ten-year-old, Mike walks through the kitchen and gets a cookie. Mom calls to him but he ignores her and leaves the room. Mom follows him and finds him playing with his baseball cards in the family room. Here's how she could use Corrective Teaching with her son.

Stop the problem behavior.

Mom: "Mike, would you please put down your cards for a minute? When I said hello to you, you ignored me. And then when I asked you to come back, you just kept walking. What's up?"

Mike: "Sometimes I don't feel like talking to people. You do that sometimes."

Mom: "I know sometimes people don't feel like talking, but you can't just blow somebody off without explaining to them that you don't feel like talking right now."

Mike: "Yeah, whatever."

Describe what you want.

Mom: "Next time you don't want to talk to somebody, you just have to say, 'I don't feel like talking right now. Can we talk later?'"

Practice what you want.

Mom: "Why don't you try that?"

Mike: "I don't feel like talking right now. Can we talk later?"

Give a consequence.

Mom: "Sure. Maybe tonight after dinner, instead of watching television, you and I can talk about what happened today while you're helping me with the dishes. Okay?"

Mike: "Oh, man!"

In this scene, Mom did several things that helped her effectively teach Mike. First, she stayed on the issue and didn't get sidetracked by any of Mike's comments. Second, she used a consequence that will effectively reduce the problem in the future, and will help develop a stronger relationship with her son. They'll spend time talking together while doing the dishes. Finally, she switched the order of the steps to make Corrective Teaching fit the situation. Mike doesn't accept consequences well so Mom saved the consequence step until after she had described and had him practice what he could do differently the next time.

EXAMPLE 3

A neighbor calls to let Dad know that she's seen his 15-year-old son driving Dad's car when he wasn't at home. Dad confronts his son with this information and finds that he took the car to the store. Here's how Dad could use Corrective Teaching with his son.

 Stop the problem behavior.

Dad: "How was your trip?"

Damien: "What trip?"

Dad: "The trip you took in my car yesterday."

Damien: "I didn't go anywhere in your car."

Dad: "Damien, Mrs. Thomas said she saw you driving away from the house in my car. Where were you going?"

Damien: "Well, I just had to go to the store. It was nothing big, Dad."

Dad: "Do you know how serious this could be? You don't have a license. Anything could have happened."

Damien: "I know how to drive, Dad. Nothing was going to happen."

Dad: "You think you know how to drive! Now the next time you go near one of the cars in this house will be *after* you pass a driver's ed course."

Give a consequence.

Dad: "And furthermore, young man, you're going to be grounded for one month and I have a list of things you need to do."

Damien: "A whole month?! It wasn't like I was driving around, Dad. I just went to the quick shop."

Dad: "Do you understand how serious this is? You could have been injured … or anything could have happened."

 Describe what you want.

Dad: "The next time you go to the quick shop, you can walk, you can ride your bike, which we've provided for you, or you can ask your mother or I to take you."

 Practice what you want.

Dad: "Now, to avoid this kind of situation in the future, what are you going to do?"

Damien: "I guess I have to ride my bike or walk."

Dad: "All right. Now listen, I've got this list of chores. You'd better get started on it. Let's go."

(Things might not go this smoothly every time you correct your children. If they start arguing or yelling, or their behavior gets worse in other ways, use the teaching method explained in the next chapter. It is a way to respond to emotionally intense situations with your children.)

In this example, Dad grounded Damien for one month. Here are a few points to remember when choosing a consequence.

➤ First, when your child is grounded, you are grounded. So make sure you use a consequence you are willing to enforce.

➤ Second, always use the smallest consequence you think will work. If this is the first time Damien's taken the car, it may have been just as effective to ground Damien for one weekend or one week. On the other hand, if taking the car has been a problem in the past or if Damien has a history of joy riding, or related activities, then one month may be right on target. Your choice of consequence should fit the seriousness and the history of the misbehavior.

➤ Third, sometimes it's best to give yourself and your child time to calm down before choosing a consequence. This gives you a chance to think about what consequence may work best. Naturally, your child does not have privileges during the time the two of you are calming down.

➤ Another way to choose a consequence is to ask your child to come up with one. Often, the consequence your child picks is more severe than the one you would choose.

Helpful Hints

➤ **Remain calm.** Remember, when misbehavior occurs, stop and think about what you need to do. Then, calm yourself and proceed with Corrective Teaching. We'll cover more about developing a plan for staying calm in the next chapter.

TIP...
If you stay calm, you'll do a better job of teaching.

Stick to one issue. Most kids are masters at getting parents sidetracked. They use lines such as:

"You don't love me!"

"My friends don't have to do that. Their parents are nice."

"You can take away anything you want. I just don't care."

These types of comments often go straight to a parent's heart. However, now is not the time for being defensive or sarcastic. Focus on what you want to teach. Let your kids know that if they really want to talk about other topics, they can bring them up after the main issue of their misbehavior is resolved.

➤ **Provide a chance to earn back some part of a consequence.** If your child is attentive and works to make up for the misbehavior, and you are pleased with the attempt, don't hesitate to give some part of the consequence back. For example, you take away one hour of TV time because your son and daughter were arguing. After you finish Corrective Teaching, both children apologize and work together to clean the dishes. If they cooperate, you could give back up to half of the TV time they lost. Doing this allows you to give them a reward for working together.

TIP...
Let your child earn back part of a consequence.

➤ **Be consistent.** This means that if the kids' bedtime is 9:30, then they should be in bed on time each night. If they get to bed on time, let them know it. Use Effective Praise and maybe some creative rewards. If they are late to bed, use Corrective Teaching and eliminate the rewards. The more consistent you are, the more consistent your children will be.

➤ **Be flexible.** What we mean is that you should consistently use Corrective Teaching, but you can vary the way you use it. No one knows your child better than you. If you think that your daughter will learn more if you put the consequence at the end of the teaching sequence, then give it a try.

➤ **Use consequences.** Some parents feel uncomfortable using consequences, even as the last step in the teaching sequence. However, consequences increase the likelihood that children will make the connection between what they did and what they get to do (or don't get to do). They come to understand that their behavior has an effect on others as well as themselves.

Summary

Rome wasn't built in a day. Nothing happens overnight. Thirty-minute miracles only happen on TV. Changing children's behavior takes time.

Parents tell us that they would like more practice with Corrective Teaching before using it with their children. So take time to practice Corrective Teaching often; for example, practice in front of the mirror, or with a friend or neighbor. Get comfortable with the steps before using them with your children. Then, use Corrective Teaching as often as possible to help your children learn quickly.

Also remember that Preventive Teaching, Effective Praise, and charts or contracts will help your children learn positive behavior more quickly. The more time you spend teaching and paying attention to the positive alternative behaviors, the quicker your children will decide to change their behavior.

Questions and Comments from Parents

Q. **What if I try to do Corrective Teaching and my child says he doesn't care what I say and leaves the house?**

A. When your child refuses to listen to you and leaves the house, use the skill Teaching Self-Control. (We'll talk about Teaching Self-Control in the next session.) For now, as long as you are comfortable that your child is safe when he leaves the house, you can wait to teach and give consequences when he returns home.

Q. **What kind of consequence is good for a boy who hits his sister?**

A. It is sometimes helpful to use a consequence that is the opposite of the problem behavior. In this case, he could do something nice with or for his sister. For example, depending on the age of the kids, he could make her bed in the morning, clean out her car, empty the trash from her bedroom, or do one of her chores. If he's older than her, he could read to her, help her with her homework, help her clean her bedroom, or practice soccer with her. If they are about the same age and he hits her because he wants a toy, losing the opportunity to play with the toy might be a good consequence to use. Time-Out also works well for younger children.

Q. **What are some consequences I can use when my child:**

A. Won't listen?

A. Actually, the problem is that your child is not following instructions. So, do Corrective Teaching and teach her how to follow instructions in Step #3. The consequence (Step #2) could be that she must do an additional chore or she loses a privilege. Again, the consequence will depend on the situation in which this behavior occurs. How often is this a problem? How serious a problem is this? How much of a problem does this create for the child and parent? What have you tried in the past? All these questions will help determine what consequence you should try.

Q. **B. Comes home late?**

A. Depending on how late and how often this is a problem, the child can come in early the next day, or lose the privilege of going out the next day. If this is a recurring problem, the child may have an earlier curfew or be allowed to go out on only one weekend night until he or she can demonstrate the ability to come home on time.

Q. **C. Fights with his brother?**

A. The two of them can do one or several chores together, play a game without fighting for 15 minutes, or practice how to work out five problems without fighting. Read the answers to the second question on this page for additional ideas for this situation.

Q. **D. Sleeps too late in the morning?**

A. He could go to bed early the next night, lose TV time the next night, or get his school things and clothes ready at night before he goes to bed.

Q. **E. Hits and kicks me and won't stop?**

A. In the next chapter, you will learn a parenting skill called Teaching Self-Control, which can be used in this situation. This skill will guide you in teaching your children how to calm down and learn how to express themselves without hitting and kicking. In the last step of Teaching Self-Control, you give a consequence for the problem behavior, which in this case is your child's hitting and kicking.

Q. **My child will argue about everything I say. She never admits anything even if I'm specific. She will just lie.**

A. Do not get sidetracked when your child argues or lies when you are correcting her. Deal with one problem behavior at a time. If you are reasonably sure she did something wrong, go ahead and do Corrective Teaching, even if she insists she didn't do it. If by chance you were wrong, then apologize to her and give back the privilege she lost for the alleged misbehavior.

Q. Sometimes I correct my child for a behavior, but when he goes to his father's house, he gets away with it. What am I to do?

A. In a perfect world, both parents would have the same expectations and be consistent with their use of consequences. In reality, there is probably very little you can do to change his father's parenting style. If you consistently use Corrective Teaching with your child's problem behavior when he is with you, then he will understand your rules. You also can use Preventive Teaching to help your son learn that different rules apply in different places. For example, there are different rules at school, church, your home, and his father's home. You might want to encourage his father to attend Common Sense Parenting classes.

Q. No consequence I use has any effect on my son's behavior. He just doesn't care.

A. One single mother with whom we worked told us that when she grounded her 15-year-old son for coming home late, it didn't matter; he was so big, he went out whenever he wanted to anyway. She felt helpless and figured there were no consequences she could use to get him to come home on time.

We helped her come up with several consequences she could use, consequences over which she had some control. These included weekly allowance, cable TV subscription, video rentals, special clothes, special snacks, and rides to movies or friends' homes.

Use consequences that you can and will enforce. This is true whether you are providing positive or negative consequences.

If your child hasn't changed his behavior after you've consistently used a consequence, then your child is letting you know that it's not the right consequence. Change the consequence. You also need to realize that even though consequences are powerful, they

alone do not change behaviors. Use all the Common Sense Parenting skills – Effective Praise to increase positive behaviors, Preventive Teaching to prevent problems, and Corrective Teaching to teach desired behaviors – to help your child change his or her behavior.

Q. My daughter just ignores everything I say when I correct her. She would never stand still for all these steps.

A. There could be many reasons why your daughter ignores you when you correct her. Perhaps she sees you as lecturing her, or repeating yourself, or yelling at her, or threatening to use consequences you never enforce. Or it could be that in the past you have allowed her to ignore you without addressing that problem effectively, so that now it is a major problem. Regardless of why she ignores you, you can teach her to do otherwise. It will take some time, effort, and persistence, but you can get her to pay attention to you when you correct her.

Start by using Preventive Teaching to teach what you expect when you are talking to her. For example, you might want her to look at you and answer questions pleasantly. If you correct her, you want her to let you know that she understands what you said and that she'll change or take care of the problem. So when you let her know that her jeans are too tight and you want her to change them, she should say, "Okay, will my green pants be okay?" Have her practice answering you like this at various times during the day. This will take some time but work with her consistently and use the steps.

Also, look for times when she looks at you and listens to what you say. This might be when you let her know that her friend is on the phone, or tell her she doesn't have to help with dishes, or ask her about a song on the radio, or when you ask her for her opinion when you're shopping together. In each situation, use Effective Praise to let her know that she is listening to you and that's what you would like her to do when you correct her, too.

Q. **If I gave my child a consequence right away, he would just blow up and leave.**

A. It's not unusual for this to happen. Sometimes, no matter how large or small the consequence, the child just lets you have it. If your child reacts like this, you may want to wait and give the consequence at the end of Corrective Teaching. When you do that, he gets to hear all you have to say before he blows up.

Another approach would be to use Preventive Teaching to teach him how you expect him to accept consequences. Use Preventive Teaching frequently and with a variety of consequences.

If your child is younger, use odd or funny consequences during this Preventive Teaching practice. For older children, set up Preventive Teaching so that they practice accepting a consequence from a teacher, coach, school principal, judge, or employer. This arrangement might take some of the emotion out of their reaction. After several practices, let them know that you expect the same kind of calm response when you give them a consequence.

Q. **How do I correct my two kids for fighting when I don't know who started it?**

A. You are in one room, your children are in the other, and all you hear is the screaming and yelling. Once you stop the fight, give them a chance to calm down. Often, they calm down more quickly when they are in separate rooms. Then, bring them together and have them take turns telling you what happened. If they start arguing again, separate them and talk with the child who is most cooperative.

Generally, if they were both fighting, they should both get a consequence, regardless of who started the fight. (They each had opportunities to stop the fight and didn't.)If they both agree that one of them started it, then that child would probably get a more serious consequence.

If possible, it can be helpful to have them work together as a consequence. They can fold a load of laundry, wash and dry the dishes, or clean out the silverware drawer. Any chore or activity that gives them the opportunity to practice getting along with each other can be very effective at this time.

Q. **What can I do when I am pretty sure my child is lying but I can't prove it?**

A. First of all, lying is a typical misbehavior for young children. Nevertheless, knowing that lying is commonplace does not make it any easier to accept it from your children. Use Corrective Teaching to address the lying whenever it occurs. Also, look for opportunities to catch your child telling the truth and use Effective Praise to encourage honesty in those situations.

When children are caught in a lie, it is rare for them to admit it at first. So don't expect it. If your child has a history of lying, and there's reason to believe he is lying, then have him prove his innocence. Examine why you think he is lying and you may find enough proof. Also, stop your child when you think he's lying and tell him to take a few minutes to think about what's happening before he tells you something that is not true and earns another consequence.

Q. **How can I correct my kids for yelling at each other when my spouse and I yell at each other or at them?**

A. Make a conscious effort to model good communication skills for your children. It's really hard to change old habits and sometimes you will make mistakes. When you do yell at each other or your children, it is helpful to apologize. Let your children know you don't want anyone to yell and then practice with them how you wish you would have handled it. It won't happen overnight, but if you really try, you and your child will see improvement.

Exercise 1 – Identifying What the Parent Did Wrong

After you watch each video example, circle the answer that identifies what the parent did wrong. Then, start the video again and compare your answer with the parents' answers in class. After each class discussion, the scene is shown again with a parent using Corrective Teaching to deal with the child's problem behavior. The dialogue from the Corrective Teaching scene follows each part of this exercise.

Children's Behavior	What Did the Parent Do Wrong?
Scene 1 Two teens arguing about the car.	a. Dad got upset and started lecturing. b. Dad offered to help with the rides. c. Dad threatened his teens. d. Dad ignored the teens' arguing.

Scene 1: Dad uses Corrective Teaching in response to his two teens arguing about who gets to use the car.

Step 1. Stop the problem behavior.

> Dad: "Stop arguing! Be quiet."

Step 2. Give a consequence.

> Dad: "Now, for arguing, the two of you together can clean out the car."

Step 3. Describe what you want.

> Dad: "When you both need the car, find out what time you both have to leave and then see if you can work something out. Adam, what time do you have to leave?"
>
> Adam: "I have to pick Mike up at 8."
>
> Katie: "My movie starts at 7:30."

Step 4. Practice what you want.

> Dad: "Okay, now without arguing, try to work something out. "
>
> Katie: "Well, could you drop me off on the way to Mike's?"
>
> Adam: "But does that mean I have to pick you up after the show's over?"
>
> Katie: "No, Jane's parents are going to do that."
>
> Adam: "Fine."
>
> Dad: "Okay, now isn't that much better? Now after you get done eating, you can start working on the car."

(Answer: a. Dad got upset and started lecturing.)

Children's Behavior	What Did the Parent Do Wrong?
Scene 2 Daughter stole makeup.	a. Mom swore at her daughter. b. Mom struck her daughter. c. Mom yelled at her daughter. d. Mom lied to her daughter.

Scene 2: Mom uses Corrective Teaching in response to finding stolen makeup in her daughter's jacket after coming home from the store.

Step 1. Stop the problem behavior.

Mom: "And where did you get these from?" *(Mom holds out a handful of makeup items.)*

Brooke: "What do you mean?"

Mom: "When I was hanging up your coat after coming home from the store, these fell out of the pocket."

Brooke: "Briana gave them to me."

Mom: "What's your second guess?"

Brooke: "I don't know."

Mom: "You don't know where you got them from. They're still in the package. You leave me no other choice but to think that you stole them."

Step 2. Give a consequence.

Mom: "So don't plan on doing anything with your friends for another month."

Brooke: "A month!"

Mom: "Yes, a month. We're going to take these back to the store, give them back, and pay them the money that you should have paid in the first place."

Brooke: "But I don't have any money."

Mom: "Well, you can do extra chores around the house during the time that you're grounded."

Step 3. Describe what you want.

Mom: "Then you can figure out how you can ask me for something when you don't have the money."

Step 4. Practice what you want.

Mom: "Show me how you would do that."

Brooke: "Mom, can you loan me a few dollars?"

Mom: "Then I would probably say, 'What do you need the money for?'"

Brooke: "I want to buy some makeup."

Mom: "Then I could probably say, 'Well, I think I could give your allowance a day ahead of time.' You see, Brooke, there are other ways to get things without stealing them."

(Answer: c. Mom yelled at her daughter.)

What do you do if your child refuses to return the merchandise? Here are some general guidelines if this happens with your child.

➤ While your child may not want to return the items or feels uncomfortable or embarrassed about returning the stolen merchandise, it is important that you do what you can to get him or her back to the store. *(Paying for the returned item reimburses the store since the item can no longer be sold as new.)* Studies have shown that returning and paying for stolen items helps reduce the likelihood of future stealing. Your child could also complete other forms of restitution such as working at the store until the debt is paid off or doing community service work of one sort or another. Also, there is a legal and moral responsibility associated with returning the stolen items. Explain this responsibility to your child so that he or she clearly understands the legal (and moral) consequences of keeping stolen goods.

➤ While having the child return stolen items is the most effective way to prevent additional thefts, your child may not willingly do so in every situation. As an alternative, you could have your child write an apology to the store manager. Then, you take the apology, the stolen items, and the money to the store manager. Or you can return the stolen items, apologize for your child's actions, pay for the items, and have the child pay you back. This payback can be in the form of doing chores around the house, baby-sitting the younger children, or losing allowance for a specified amount of time.

➤ Like Brooke in the last scene, parents also find it helpful to have their child lose the privilege of going to the store, mall, or out with friends for a certain amount of time *(in addition to returning items to the store)*. After Brooke returns and pays for the stolen items, her parents can determine whether she would earn back some of the privilege of going out with her friends.

➤ In the next chapter, we discuss a skill called Teaching Self-Control. Parents use Teaching Self-Control when their children won't respond to Corrective Teaching *(refusing to return stolen merchandise)* or have sudden or intense emotional outbursts. It's also useful in situations where parents feel like they're going to blow up at their children.

Exercise 2 – Selecting a Consequence and Skill

Watch the scene and pause the video. First, select the consequence that seems like the best choice for this situation. Second, match the description of the behavior on the left with the correct skill on the right. Finally, watch the class discussion to check your answers.

If you have questions about selecting negative consequences, refer to Chapter 1 in this book or Session 1 of this video series.

After each class discussion, the scene is shown again with a parent using Corrective Teaching to deal with the child's problem behavior. The dialogue from the Corrective Teaching scene follows each part of this exercise.

Children's Behavior	**What's the Best Consequence?**
Scene 1 Daughter has friends over when parents aren't home.	a. No telephone rest of evening. b. Wash and put away the dishes. c. Stay home with no friends visiting for one week. d. No consequence; it was no big deal.

Children's Behavior	**What Social Skill Would You Teach?**
Scene 1 Daughter has friends over when parents aren't home.	a. How to ask permission. b. How to get along with friends. c. How to get homework completed. d. How to accept "No" answers.

Scene 1: Mom comes home and finds her daughter's friends leaving the house. They have a family rule that states that friends cannot be at the house when a parent isn't home. Mom uses Corrective Teaching to let her daughter know what she can do next time instead of having the friends over to the house.

Step 1. Stop the problem behavior.

Mom: "What were Tim and Jessie doing here?"

Tina: "Nobody was here Mom."

Mom: "Tina, I saw them leaving as I came home. Now, let's try this one more time. What were they doing here?"

Tina: "They came home from school with me."

Mom: "Tina, you know you are not supposed to have friends over when we're not home. You didn't ask permission."

Step 2. Give a consequence.

Mom: "Now, because of this, you're not going to be going out tonight or tomorrow night."

Tina: "Mom, I don't see what the big deal is? We didn't do anything wrong, we were just listening to music and hanging out. You treat me like a little kid. I can't do anything."

Step 3. Describe what you want.

Mom: "Tina, we would love to have you go out, but you need to ask permission."

Step 4. Practice what you want.

Mom: "Now, what would happen if Sarah wants to come over after school, what should happen?"

Tina: "Ask you first."

Mom: "That's right. And she needs to get permission from her parents. And I need to know how long she's going to be here, how she's going to get here, and how she's going to get back home. These questions need to be answered before I give permission."

Tina: "It feels like the police."

Mom: "I'm sure it does. But remember, I still can say 'No' if an adult is not going to be around."

Tina: "You are so old-fashioned!"

(Answer: c. Stay home with no friends visiting for one week, and a. How to ask permission)

Children's Behavior	What's the Best Consequence?
Scene 2 Two children arguing about the coloring book.	a. Go to their room for one hour. b. Clean the kitchen together. c. Sit in Time-Out for five minutes. d. No coloring for half an hour.

Children's Behavior	What Social Skill Would You Teach?
Scene 2 Two children arguing about the coloring book.	a. How to share your feelings. b. How to ask for help. c. How to share your toys. d. How to disagree in a nice way.

Scene 2: Two sisters are fighting over a coloring book. Dad uses Corrective Teaching to let the older daughter know what she can do next time instead of grabbing the book from her sister.

Step 1. Stop the problem behavior.

> *Dad:* "Okay, girls, give me that coloring book. All right, let me have the book. Look at it. You tore it. Niosha, it sounds like you had the coloring book first. Is that right?"
>
> *Niosha:* "Yeah, and she tried to grab it from me."
>
> *Dad:* "Alisha, is that right?"
>
> *Alisha:* "But she always gets it first!"

Step 2. Give a consequence.

> *Dad:* "Okay, Alisha, for grabbing the book from Niosha, you won't get to color in it for a half hour."
>
> *Alisha:* "Aw, Dad."

Step 3. Describe what you want.

> *Dad:* "Alisha, if you want the book Niosha has, just ask her nicely for it. If she says no, just get another book and color in that one for a while."

Step 4. Practice what you want.

> *Dad:* "Let's give that a try. Go ahead, ask her."
>
> *Alisha:* "Niosha, can I borrow your book?"
>
> *Niosha:* "No, you can't."
>
> *Dad::* "Okay, see, you didn't argue; you didn't yell; and you can play in that book for a while until she's finished with the other one."

In this scene, Dad took time to find out that it was Alisha who started the fight. Some parents prefer to give consequences to both girls, since both were fighting. If Dad had used this approach, he could have had them do a chore together or had both of them lose the privilege of coloring for a half hour. Then, he could teach them both to share and take turns with the coloring book.

(Answer: d. No coloring for half an hour, and c. How to share your toys)

Children's Behavior	What's the Best Consequence?
Scene 3 Daughter watching TV before homework is completed.	a. No TV for rest of the night. b. Help Mom with dishes. c. No phone calls until homework is finished. d. Get extra credit school work from teacher.

Children's Behavior	What Social Skill Would You Teach?
Scene 3 Daughter watching TV before homework is completed.	a. How to get someone's attention. b. How to accept "No" answers. c. How to control your anger. d. How to follow instructions.

Scene 3: Jennifer is watching TV instead of doing her homework as asked. Mom uses Corrective Teaching to teach Jennifer how to follow instructions right away.

Step 1. Stop the problem behavior.

Mom: "Jennifer Marie!! Look, I know you'd rather watch TV, but you are supposed to be doing your homework. So, get the TV turned off and go get started on your homework. "

Jennifer: "Can't I do it later?"

Mom: "No, Jenny, turn the TV off now and get your books out."

Jennifer: "Why can't I just watch this and then do my homework?"

Step 2. Give a consequence.

Mom: "All right, Jenny, since you're watching TV instead of doing your homework, you can just skip TV the rest of tonight."

Jennifer: "Even when I'm done?"

Mom: "Even when you're done."

Step 3. Describe what you want.

Mom: "All you have to do is go get started on your homework right away when I tell you to. Just tell me, 'All right, Mom.' And get going. Understand?"

Jennifer: "All right, Mom."

Step 4. Practice what you want.

Mom: "Good. Now, turn the TV off, get your books out, and let's get going."

Jennifer: "Fine."

(Answer: a. No TV for the rest of the night, and d. How to follow instructions)

Homework 1 – Corrective Teaching

Please write three misbehaviors your child did. Record how you responded using the steps of Corrective Teaching.

Behavior: _____

1. Stop the problem behavior. _____
   _____

2. Give a consequence. _____
   _____

3. Describe what you want. _____
   _____

4. Practice what you want. _____
   _____

Behavior: _____

1. Stop the problem behavior. _____
   _____

2. Give a consequence. _____
   _____

3. Describe what you want. _____
   _____

4. Practice what you want. _____
   _____

Behavior: _____

1. Stop the problem behavior. _____
   _____

2. Give a consequence. _____
   _____

3. Describe what you want. _____
   _____

4. Practice what you want. _____
   _____

CHAPTER 5

Handling Emotionally Intense Situations

In this chapter we'll be learning about ways to:

➤ Stay calm when your children are pushing your buttons.

➤ Teach your children how to express their feelings in ways that are helpful to them and the rest of the family. We call this parenting skill "Teaching Self-Control."

"That's all you ever say, 'We'll talk about it later.' What a jerk!"

"You're a complete idiot. I hate you!"

"Get outta my face!"

"No way! I ain't gonna do it, and you can't make me!"

One of the more frustrating aspects of parenting is dealing with your children when they become angry or defiant, or simply refuse to do what you ask. They may be yelling, hitting, arguing, throwing objects, or threatening you. At times like these, parents can feel emotionally drained, powerless, or just plain furious!

If you've ever felt like this, you're not alone. All parents experience these situations at one time or another, and some parents face them frequently. One thing is certain, however: Kids must learn that negative, aggressive behavior is not acceptable. The sooner kids learn how to handle these situations without hurting themselves or others, the more successful they'll be at home, in school, and in relationships.

Staying Calm

Parents tell us that the biggest challenge they face in dealing with their child's problem behaviors is staying calm. Kids can be sarcastic, defiant, rebellious, and sometimes even violent. Parents have to prepare themselves for times like these and learn to stay calm.

> **TIP...**
> Be prepared. Have a plan for staying calm.

Many parents say that when they are angry, they yell or swear at their kids. Some say that they hit something, or throw or kick things. They are convinced that these angry responses work to show their kids they "mean business." And these responses do temporarily stop their children's problem behavior. But what do their children learn? They learn to yell, hit, and throw or kick things when upset.

As these parents go through our Common Sense Parenting classes, they learn to stay calm in tense situations and they report the following results:

1. Their kids' temper tantrums or problem behaviors stop sooner.

2. Their kids' problem behaviors aren't as severe.

3. They feel better about the way they handle the situation.

Steps to Staying Calm

Three steps in developing your 'Staying Calm' plan

To help you keep your cool in these intense situations, we'll help you lay out a plan for staying calm.

1. Identify what your children do that gets you upset.

2. Identify early warning signals that tell you that you're getting upset.

3. Decide what you can do to stay calm.

 Identify what your children do that gets you upset.

The first step in being able to respond calmly to your kids' problem behaviors is knowing what makes you angry. Typically, kids know just what words or actions annoy us.

You may get angry when your child turns around and walks away from you while you're talking, or when your child screams "Shut up!" at his sister. When parents can specify children's problem behaviors that get them angry, they're more likely to respond calmly and help their children's behavior improve.

Here is what other parents have said bothers them:

➤ When my kids swear at me.

➤ When my kids argue because they can't have things their way.

➤ When my stepkids tell me I'm not their real dad.

➤ When my teenager just starts yelling whenever I ask her to do something around the home.

➤ When, after a long day at work, my kids bombard me with questions like "What's for dinner?" or "Can I go over to Rafael's house?" or "Why do I have to clean my room?"

➤ When my 8-year-old has a tantrum when we're all in a rush in the morning before work and school.

➤ When my teenager comes home late and then acts as if I'm the problem because I'm the only parent who enforces a curfew.

➤ When I ask my kids to help with something and they ignore me, almost like they're waiting for me to forget that I asked for help.

(Complete Step 1 in Exercise 1 at the end of this chapter.)

 Identify early warning signals that tell you that you're getting upset.

The second step is recognizing early warning signals that tell us we're getting angry. This allows us to think before we act and remain calm.

What are your warning signals? Does your heart race or your face get flushed? Do you clench your teeth, make a fist, or feel your muscles tighten? Do you talk faster or louder or start pointing and making abrupt movements? Take some time to think about the early warning signs that tell you that you're beginning to get upset.

Here's what other parents have told us.

➤ "My heart starts pounding and my voice gets really shaky."

➤ "I start shaking my hands and waving my arms."

➤ "I get so angry that I'm afraid I'm going to shake or slap my kids."

➤ "I get a knot in my stomach."

➤ "My hands get sweaty."

➤ "I start talking faster."

(Complete Step 2 in Exercise 1 at the end of this chapter.)

Decide what you can do to stay calm.

In the past when you've been upset with your children, you may have yelled or fought or argued with them. In this third step, you can decide what you can do instead of staying in the fight with your children. It's not always easy to do this step, but if you can come up with a plan, you'll be much more likely to take care of those child behavior problems without making them worse.

Let's take a look at what parents have told us works for them.

➤ "I take a deep breath and count to 10 – or 100."

➤ "I go for a walk."

➤ "When my kids are yelling at me and following me around the house, I lock myself in the bedroom to catch my breath."

➤ "I put my hands in my pockets. I tend to talk with my hands, especially when I'm angry. Before I learned to do this, I think my daughter thought I was going to hit her."

➤ "I sit down because if I'm standing, I begin to tremble. I can still tell my child what he's doing wrong, but I say it a lot more calmly."

➤ "I just leave the situation for awhile. I go to another room until I can handle my feelings."

➤ "I wear a rubber band on my wrist and snap the band whenever I feel like I'm getting upset. That's a signal to myself that I'd better calm down."

➤ "I call someone like my best friend or my sister. By talking about the situation, I can go back in and deal with it more calmly."

(Complete Step 3 in Exercise 1 at the end of this chapter.)

The Plan for Staying Calm

Let's see how other parents have combined the three steps to come up with their Plan for Staying Calm.

➤ When my kids start yelling and they start swearing and cursing at me *(child's problem behavior)*, and I can feel my heart pounding and my voice starts to get shaky *(early warning signals)*, I'm just going to walk away and then I know that I can avoid yelling *(what I can do differently)*.

➤ When my kids complain to their father about how mean I am *(child's problem behavior)*, and before I start yelling *(early warning signals)*, I'll tell them I'm upset and then I'll go for a walk *(what I can do differently)*.

➤ The next time my son talks back to me and refuses to go to bed *(child's problem behavior)*, and my heart starts to pound *(early warning signals)*, I will take a deep breath and let it out slowly before I correct him *(what I can do differently)*.

➤ The next time my kids complain about all the work they have to do *(child's problem behavior)*, and I think I'm going to explode *(early warning signals)*, I will call my sister and talk with her before going back and using Corrective Teaching with the kids *(what I can do differently)*.

➤ When my kids get my spouse and I to argue about consequences for what they did wrong *(child's problem behavior)*, and I start yelling at my spouse *(early warning signals)*, I will go to the bedroom and calm down before talking calmly to my spouse about what we can do *(what I can do differently)*.

(Now, complete your plan in Exercise 1 at the end of this chapter.)

Learning to stay calm in those emotionally intense situations with your children will take some time. Don't get discouraged if you lose your temper every now and then. Just try to do better the next time – and with kids, there almost always will be a next time!

Helpful Hints

➤ **Practice positive thinking.** If you find yourself thinking negative thoughts, interrupt those thoughts. Say "Stop it!" to yourself. Then refocus with positive thoughts.

Here are some examples of positive thoughts that other parents have used:

"Relax. Take it easy."

"I am going to help my child."

"I'm a good parent, and I can do this."

"It's going to get better. It just takes time."

➤ **Don't take what your child says personally.** This may be very difficult when your child is calling you names. Learn how to let negative, angry comments bounce off you, and the effectiveness of your teaching will increase. Take time to sit down and talk with your child after he or she is calm if you are concerned about something your child says while upset.

➤ **Use the "take five" rule.** Instead of blurting out an angry response, take five minutes to think about what is happening.

➤ **Focus on behavior instead of what you think are the reasons for your child's misbehavior.** When you're in the heat of an argument, don't try to analyze your child's behavior; instead, look for ways to help your child and yourself calm down. After you solve the problem, take the time to talk to your child about what happened and why.

➤ **If you get angry and say or do something you regret, go back and say you're sorry.** This sets a good example for your children to follow when they make a mistake. Apologize, say what you did wrong, and what you're going to do differently next time. Some parents worry about apologizing to their children because parents think it causes them to lose some of their parental control. We've found apologizing helps kids realize that everyone, young and old alike, makes mistakes.

TIP...
When you stay calm, your child calms down more quickly.

➤ **Staying calm does not mean you are totally passive.** There are times when you will raise your voice – but it should be a firm, no-nonsense voice tone. And the words you use should be specific descriptions, not judgments, put-downs, or negative feelings. Staying calm means not reacting to misbehavior in an angry, aggressive manner.

➤ **Take care of the problem with your child.** Calming down is the first step toward resolving the problem that resulted in the emotional outburst from you or your children. In this next section, we will discuss how to teach your children to express their angry and upset feelings in helpful ways. Once they're able to share their feelings in constructive ways, they're more likely to resolve problems before a crisis arises.

Teaching Self-Control

You've had a hard day at work. While you try to make something that resembles dinner, you're thinking of the things you have to do during the next six hours. You'd like just a little help, so you ask the kids to get the table ready for dinner. They continue watching the TV and pretend they don't hear you. You yell at them to shut off the TV and get their buns out in the kitchen now! They start complaining. You start yelling. And the next thing you know, you're wrestling with them, trying to get the TV remote control out of their hands. You finally get the remote, and yell at them loud enough to shatter windows three city blocks away. They yell back at you as one storms out the front door and the other heads to her room.

Unfortunately, most parents and children have found themselves in these situations, where they're emotionally stressed and find themselves doing and saying things they later regret. In these situations, the longer parents argue and fight with the child, the worse the situation gets. At times like these, we recommend a parenting skill called Teaching Self-Control.

When to Use Teaching Self-Control

Parents can use Teaching Self-Control in three types of situations:

➤ When their children misbehave and will not respond to Corrective Teaching; instead, the children continue or the misbehavior gets worse.

➤ When their children "blow up" – a sudden and intense emotional outburst – and refuse to do anything that the parents ask.

➤ When parents are too upset with their children and feel like they're going to blow up.

Think of the last time your children got upset when you corrected their behavior or asked them to do something. What triggered their negative behavior? How did you respond? Looking back at past "blow-ups" can help you plan for how to deal with them in the future. One way to prevent blow-ups is to combine your plan for staying calm with the steps of Teaching Self-Control.

Steps for Teaching Self-Control

The goals of Teaching Self-Control are to:

➤ Help you and your children calm down during emotionally intense situations.

➤ Teach your children how to control their behavior when they get upset.

Teaching Self-Control has two main parts. Part One is Calming Down and Part Two is Follow-Up Teaching. Each of these two parts has three steps. You have already learned most of these steps.

Part One: Calming Down

1. Describe the problem behavior.

2. Give clear instructions.

3. Allow time to calm down.

Part Two: Follow-Up Teaching

4. Describe what your child can do differently next time.

5. Practice what your child can do next time.

6. Give a consequence.

Part One: Calming Down

 Describe the problem behavior.

Briefly tell your child exactly what he or she is doing wrong. We emphasize "briefly" here. Remember to be clear and specific with what you say. You should talk in a calm, slow, level voice tone. For example, saying "Marcus, you're yelling at me and pacing around the room," gives the child a clear message about what he is doing. Describe what your child is doing wrong without becoming angry, sarcastic, or accusatory.

It also helps to use empathy when your child is upset or angry. Empathy means showing understanding for the other person's feelings. For instance, you might say, "It looks like you're upset right now. And I know you're unhappy with what happened." This starts the teaching sequence positively and shows your child that you really do care about his or her feelings. Using empathy often helps you focus on your child's behavior rather than your own emotions.

Give clear instructions.

The purpose of this step is to tell your child exactly what he or she needs to do to begin calming down. These instructions often give the child a choice, such as, "Please go to your room or sit on the porch and calm down." Or make calming statements to your child like, "Take a few deep breaths and try to settle down." Don't give too many instructions or repeat them frequently. Use simple, clear options that keep the focus on having your child regain self-control.

 Allow time to calm down.

If parents remain calm, it increases the likelihood that their child will calm down faster and helps parents focus on their child's behavior. Simply saying, "We both need a little time to calm down. I'll be back in a few minutes," can be very effective. Remember, sometimes giving your child a little "space" helps your child "save face."

As parents take the time to calm down, they can think of what they are going to teach next. This time also allows the child to make a decision – to continue misbehaving or to cooperate.

Come back to the child as often as necessary. Ask questions like, "Can we talk about what happened?" or "Are you calm enough to talk to me?" or "Are you ready to take care of the problem?"

Move to "Part Two: Follow-Up Teaching" when your child is able to answer you in a reasonably calm voice and is paying attention to what you say. Take your time. Give descriptions and instructions as needed. Most of all, stay calm and think about what you say and do.

Part Two: Follow-Up Teaching

 Describe what your child can do differently next time.

Now that you and your child are calm, discuss other ways that your child can express frustration or anger. Kids have to learn that when they yell or fight when they're upset, they actually hurt their chances of getting to do what they want. They also must understand that their arguing, swearing, and throwing things lead to more serious problems and consequences.

If parents are having a hard time getting started with this step, we teach them the "Instead of..." phrase. It goes like this:

"Instead of yelling and running out the door the next time you get upset, please tell me you're mad and ask if you can go to your room to calm down."

"Instead of swearing, ask if you can sit on the porch until you are ready to talk about it."

Be sure to focus on what your child can do instead of blowing-up. For example, your son comes home 30 minutes late from visiting a friend. You begin Corrective Teaching and give him a consequence for coming home late. He yells at you and starts saying that he'll stay out as late as he wants. Now is the time to use Teaching Self-Control.

When you get to the fourth step of Teaching Self-Control, it's important that you teach him what to do the next time he gets upset, not the next time he comes in late. Once you teach him how to let you know he's upset, then you can go back to helping him learn how to come home on time.

5 Practice what your child can do next time.

Now that your child knows what to do, it's important that he or she knows how to do it. Have your child practice letting you know that he or she is upset. After the practice is over, tell your child what was done correctly and what needs improvement. Be as positive as you can, especially if your child is making an honest effort to do what you ask.

6 Give a consequence.

This is a crucial part of Teaching Self-Control. If there is a common mistake made by the parents we work with, it is that they forget to give a consequence. Please remember that consequences help change behavior; use them.

We emphasize that you consistently use a negative consequence at the end of each Teaching Self-Control interaction. Consequences increase the effectiveness of your teaching.

The consequence you give in this step is for the yelling, fighting, arguing, or whatever your child did that was a problem. This consequence can be large or small, depending on what your child did or how long the tantrum or yelling continued. Generally, you have already given your child a consequence for the original problem (for example, coming home late or fighting with his sister). The consequence you give now is for the most recent problem behavior – the yelling at you.

Let's take a look at several examples of Teaching Self-Control to see how these steps work.

EXAMPLE 1

In this first example, two children are fighting about a card game. Mom separates them to help them calm down and then gets them back together for the Follow-Up Teaching.

Part One: Calming Down

 1 Describe the problem behavior.

Alisha: "Anthony, that's my card!"

Anthony: "You're going to lose any way, so just shut up and play."

Alisha: "You make me sick."

Anthony: "Shut up, wart face."

Mom: "Anthony and Alisha, you both are arguing and yelling and you need to calm down right now."

Alisha: "I'm going to tell everyone at school that you play with dolls."

Anthony: "And I'm going to kick your butt!"

 2 Give clear instructions.

Mom: "Anthony, listen. I want you to go to your room or go sit in the living room."

Anthony: "I'll be glad to get out of here!"

Mom: "And Alisha, I want you to go to your room or you can sit right there."

Alisha: "I'll stay right here, but Mom, can I say one more thing?"

Anthony: "Oh sure, you're going to both gang up on me now."

 3 Allow time to calm down.

Mom: "All right! We're going to talk, but right now let's just take a break."

Mom gives both kids some time to calm down. Then, when they look like they're ready to discuss the situation, Mom gets them back together.

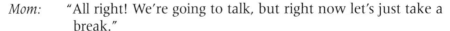

Part Two: Follow-Up Teaching

 4 Describe what your child could do differently next time.

Mom: "All right Anthony, it looks like you're a little calmer. Alisha, come in here and sit down. All right, I think we're ready to work things out, but before either one of you talk, I want you both to listen to me."

Anthony: "Oh, here we go again."

Alisha: "Do we have to?"

Mom: "Yes, we do have to. Or you can go back and sit where you were and waste the rest of your day."

Anthony: "Let's just get it over with."

Mom: "I know sometimes it's hard when you get angry at each other, but fighting and arguing only make it worse. You should just take a break from each other."

Anthony: "Sure, Mom, it's easy for you to say. You don't have her bugging you every second."

Mom: "I know sometimes it's hard to calm down, but the more you work at it, the better you're going to be at it. Okay? And then you can work out your problems without fighting and you will stay out of trouble. Okay?"

Anthony: "Yeah."

Mom: "Okay, let's just try something real quick. Let's say you two are getting angry. Alisha, what I want you to do is just say, 'Break,' and Anthony, you can say, 'Okay.' Got it?"

5 Practice what your child can do next time.

Mom: "Let's just say you're getting angry over this pencil. What are you going to say, Alisha?"

Alisha: "Break."

Mom: "And Anthony?"

Anthony: "Okay... Mom, are we done yet?"

6 Give a consequence.

Mom: "No, not yet. You guys know that when you argue over something and start fighting you're going to have to help each other with a chore. So let's get started on these dishes over here."

Mom does a nice job of separating the two children long enough for them each to calm down. Then she brings them back together for the Follow-Up Teaching. She also uses a consequence that gets them working together. This gives them an opportunity to show Mom that they've learned how to get along with each other and take a break from each other when their tempers flare. Mom can choose a consequence that keeps them apart if she thinks that would be better for her sanity and theirs.

EXAMPLE 2

Dad is in a hurry to get his older daughter to soccer practice. He lets his younger daughter, Sarah, know that it's time to leave for practice. Sarah wants to stay home. Dad starts Corrective Teaching and gets through the first two steps, "Stop the Problem Behavior" and "Give a Consequence." He then takes Sarah by the shoulders and leaves for soccer practice, using the ride to and from practice to help Sarah get calm.

Corrective Teaching

 1 Stop the problem behavior.

Dad: "Come on, Sarah. We've got to get your sister to soccer practice. Put your coat on, and let's go."

Sarah: "I'm not going!"

Dad: "Sarah, I can't leave you here. It will just take a few minutes. Please! You can play when you get back."

Sarah: "No! I'm not going."

Dad: "Sarah, put your coat on and let's go!!"

Sarah: "No!"

 2 Give a consequence.

Dad: (Dad is trying his best to stay calm.) "Sarah, because you're giving me a hard time, you're going to sit for five minutes when we get home. Now, come on!"

Sarah: "No! I'm not going!"

Dad: (Dad puts the coat on Sarah.) "And when we get back, you can't ride your pony."

Sarah: "I don't have a pony."

Dad: "I know, but if you did, you couldn't ride it because of the trouble you're giving me. Come on!"

Sarah: "I'm not going!"

Teaching Self-Control, Part One: Calming Down

At this point, Dad would switch from Corrective Teaching to Teaching Self-Control and use the ride to soccer practice as time to calm down. During the ride, just like any time you are trying to help a child calm down, Dad would not argue with Sarah. He could calmly let her know that he understands why she'd rather play than drive Jennifer to practice. He could also ask her to take a few deep breaths and calm down. And he can let her know that they can talk about how she feels about the situation after she calms down. Then, when Dad gets home, he can begin Follow-Up Teaching with Sarah.

Part Two: Follow-Up Teaching

 Describe what your child could do differently next time.

Dad: "Listen, Sarah, when you get upset, or when anyone gets upset, the thing to do is take a deep breath, count to 10, and tell me you're upset. Like this. *(Dad takes a deep breath and lets the air out while counting to 10.)* Then say, 'Dad, I'm really upset because I want to play and I don't want to go to Jennifer's practice.'"

Sarah: "Then can I stay home?"

Dad: "No, but at least then we can talk about it and we wouldn't have this big fight and you'd have more time to play."

 Practice what your child can do next time.

Dad: "So let me see you try that. Take a deep breath and tell me you're upset."

Sarah: *(Sarah takes a deep breath and lets it out while counting to 10.)* "Daddy, I'm mad because I didn't get to stay home."

Dad: "Okay. See, it works, but you have to say that and we have to talk about it."

 Give a consequence.

Dad: "Now, you still have to sit for five minutes for arguing and refusing to go. And because we were late for practice, you've got to help Jennifer with the dishes tonight."

It's not easy to stay calm when you're in a rush and kids won't cooperate. You're trying to do things for them, and it seems like they're doing little to help you. If Dad uses his staying calm plan and takes a few deep breaths, then he's more likely to handle this situation without blowing up at Sarah.

> **TIP...** Think: how did my actions fuel this fight?

Dad could have done a couple of other things to help the situation go more smoothly. First, he could have offered Sarah the option of taking a few of her toys with her for the ride. This might have been enough of a compromise to keep Sarah from refusing to go.

Second, Dad could have taken a few deep breaths and stayed calm. Children will often mirror what they see parents doing. So, if parents are in a hurry, getting excited, and talking quickly, then kids are likely to increase the tempo of their response. When that response is "NO!" and kids keep repeating that same message, it's easy for parents to get even more upset. Parents and children fuel each other's fires and next thing you know, everyone is burning.

Third, Dad could have planned to leave earlier for Jennifer's soccer practice. This is probably not the first time that Sarah has refused to get in the car when asked. If Dad has more time to get to practice, he'll be more likely to handle the situation calmly.

Fourth, Dad can start preparing Sarah for the trip to practice before it's time to go. An hour before they need to leave, Dad can use Preventive Teaching to teach Sarah what she needs to do when she's asked to go to the practice. Dad can teach Sarah the social skills, "How to Follow Instructions" or "How to Accept Parents' Answers." There are going to be times when Sarah must go along for the ride (or to other activities) because Dad can't leave her at home. Sarah needs to learn to do what's asked at those times, without arguing.

After the parent and child take care of the problem it helps to look at what each person could have done differently to prevent the problem. Parents and children are more likely to avoid those problems if they look for ways to change their behavior so that problem situations occur less often in the future.

EXAMPLE 3

Joe, a teenager, asks to go to a friend's home. Mom says that he has to finish his chores first. Joe yells and argues with his mom before leaving the house and going to his friend's home. Mom begins using Teaching Self-Control, then finishes her teaching when Joe returns home.

Part One: Calming Down

 1 Describe the problem behavior.

Joe:	"Mom, I'm going to Mike's."
Mom:	"Wait a minute Joe. Did you get all your chores finished around here?"
Joe:	"Yeah, I cleaned my room and started the laundry. I'll do the yard work later."
Mom:	"No, Joe, that's not the deal. You need to get all of your chores finished before you leave to go anywhere."
Joe:	"Well, it's not going to happen. I'll finish things later. I'm going to Mike's now."
Mom:	"Joe, you know the deal: You get to do what you want to do after you get your chores finished. Now just call Mike and tell him you'll be over there later."
Joe:	"No, I'm going now! I'm not going later. The world's not going to end if the chores aren't done right away!"
Mom:	"Joe, you are not doing what I asked you to do...."
Joe:	"To !*#@! with you!!"
Mom:	"...and you are yelling at me."
Joe:	"You do the stupid chores!"

2 Give clear instructions.

Mom:	"Listen, I want you to take a minute to take a few deep breaths and calm down."
Joe:	*(Yelling as he walks out of the door.)* "You calm down! I'm going to Mike's."

3 Allow time to calm down.

Both Mom and Joe are very upset at this point. In order to avoid even bigger problems, Mom allows Joe to leave the house without getting in his way. Mom uses this time to calm down and hopes that Joe calms down, too.

Part Two: Follow-Up Teaching

 Describe what your child could do differently next time.

Joe returns from Mike's house and walks through the kitchen where Mom and Jennifer are seated. Mom greets Joe with, "Hi, Joe. We need to talk." Joe says nothing and continues walking through the kitchen toward his bedroom. Mom follows him into his room.

Mom: "Joe, can we talk about what happened before you went to Mike's?"

Joe: "Mom, I said I'd do the chores, and I'll do them. I don't know why you make such a big fuss out of everything."

Mom: "Joe, I'm not talking about the chores, I'm talking about how you yelled at me and argued and walked out of the house."

Joe: "Well, I was mad. You never listen to me. Everything always has to be your way."

Mom: "All right, Joe, I know you'd rather go to Mike's house than do your chores. But you can't argue with me and yell at me whenever you don't get your own way. Now, we've talked about this before. What can you do instead of arguing and yelling?"

Joe: "I know, I know. I can take a few deep breaths and tell you that I'm angry. But that's hard to do when I'm mad."

Mom: "I know it's hard, but if you take a minute to take some deep breaths, then I'll listen to you and maybe we can work things out. And you won't get yourself into more trouble."

Joe: "All right, all right."

 Practice what your child can do next time.

Mom: "Okay, so let's try this whole thing over again. Let's say you want to go to Mike's now, and I'm telling you that you need to finish your chores first. What are you going to say?"

Joe: "Mom, I know I need to do the chores but can I please do them later?"

Mom: "That's right. That's all you need to say, Joe. I'm not going to listen to you if you're yelling at me, but if you're calm, then maybe we can work things out. So please try to remember that the next time instead of arguing. Okay?"

Joe: "I'll try."

 Give a consequence.

Mom: "All right. Now, because you argued and you went to Mike's without my permission, you can't use the car this weekend. Why don't you get started finishing those chores."

Many parents have asked us what they should do when their child leaves the home in the heat of an argument. While the ultimate goal is to get your children to work out the problem without leaving home, this may take some time, depending on you and your children's history of problem-solving.

TIP... Teach your children to solve – not run from – their problems.

Children who leave home generally do so to escape or avoid dealing with the problem. Teaching Self-Control helps parents teach their children how to deal with their problems without the emotionally explosive fights.

When your child leaves home during an argument, problems can get worse. While the vast majority of children return when they leave after a fight, their time on the street can be dangerous. For these reasons, we encourage parents to do what they can – without risking harm to themselves or their children – to help their children decide to stay home.

For older children and teens, we encourage parents to say something like, "You're upset. It's not easy, but I'd like you to stay to work it out. Leaving's not going to help." Or, "Come on, you're bright, go cool off in your room and we'll get this taken care of." Or "Walking out's not going to help. Think about what you're doing. I'd really like you to stay." Or, "You're smart. You know leaving won't help solve the problem. I don't want you out there when you're so upset."

It may be difficult, but holding or hugging your teens at this time may help them calm down. However, if your teen is physically aggressive, then trying to hold him is not a good idea right now. But if your teen is emotionally upset and has not been physically aggressive with you in the past, then holding may be helpful at this time.

Holding younger children to help them calm down is also a good option, especially if they have not had a history of hitting, kicking, or biting. Often, your touch and calming words can be a big help to the child – and to you. Do all you can to keep your younger children from leaving the home, since being on the streets is even more dangerous for them than for older children and teens.

It may not be easy, but try talking in a calm voice when you're telling your children that you want them to stay. Children will, in time, match your mood and tone. So the calmer you can be, the more likely it is that they will calm down.

EXAMPLE 4

Brandon is watching TV while he should be doing his homework. His father calls to him from the other room and tells him to shut off the TV. Brandon argues with his father, and refuses to shut off the TV and start on his homework. Dad uses Teaching Self-Control instead of fighting with Brandon.

Part One: Calming Down

 1 Describe the problem behavior.

> *Dad:* "Brandon, I asked you a half hour ago to get started on your homework and you're still watching TV."
>
> *Brandon:* "The show's almost over. I'll do my homework later."
>
> *Dad:* "Just for that, turn the TV off and leave it off until you get done with your homework."
>
> *Brandon:* "I said the show's almost over! I'll do my homework later." *(Dad enters the room and turns off the TV.)* "What are you doing?!"
>
> *Dad:* "Homework comes first. Then you can watch TV if you have extra time."
>
> *Brandon:* *(Brandon uses the remote control to turn on the TV.)* "I said I'll do it later!"
>
> *Dad:* *(Dad turns off the TV.)* "Leave it off!"
>
> *Brandon:* *(Brandon turns it back on.)* "No!"
>
> *Dad:* *(Dad turns off the TV again.)* "I said to leave it off!"
>
> *Brandon:* *(Brandon turns it back on.)* "No!"
>
> *Dad:* *(Dad goes toward Brandon.)* "Give me the remote."
>
> *Brandon:* *(Brandon crosses his arms and stuffs the remote under his arm.)* "Get it yourself."

2 Give clear instructions.

> *Dad:* *(Dad is mad but he's doing his best to keep anger in check.)* "Tell you what, I'm going to leave for a little bit. I want you to think of what you can do to resolve these problems because you're causing a lot of them for yourself."

3 Allow time to calm down.

Dad leaves the room to give both of them time to calm down.

Part Two: Follow-Up Teaching

 Describe what your child could do differently next time.

Dad: "Your show's over, huh?"

Brandon: "Yeah."

Dad: "Are you ready to talk about this?"

Brandon: "Talk about what?"

Dad: "Talk about how you can let me know when you're upset so we don't start a fight."

Brandon: "Whatever."

Dad: "The next time you're upset, don't shove the remote under your arm. Just let me know you're upset. Tell me and I'll give you some time to yourself."

Brandon: "Why can't you just leave me alone?"

Dad: "I could, but other people aren't going to know when you're upset. You have to be able to let people know when you're upset. They can't guess."

Practice what your child can do next time.

Dad: "So show me how you're going to let me know next time."

Brandon: "Can you just give me some space?"

Dad: "That's much better than starting a fight. I'd probably say, 'Yeah, I can give you some space…on the porch or in your room. And I'd say, 'Let me know when you're ready to talk about it.'"

Brandon: "Okay."

Give a consequence.

Dad: "But right now you've got some homework to do and no TV for an hour. And for trying to start a fight with me, you have to help me wash the car."

Brandon: "Wash the car!"

Dad: "Yes, wash the car."

Brandon: "Okay, fine."

Parents often ask why Brandon's Dad allowed him to watch TV instead of doing his homework. We understand their concern and ask them to think through their options when faced with similar situations. Let's take another look at the scenario.

1. Dad starts by asking Brandon to shut off the TV. Brandon argues and leaves it on.

2. Next, Dad comes into the room and manually shuts off the TV. Brandon turns it back on using the remote control. This on-off exchange happens several times.

3. Finally, Dad gets so frustrated that he tries to wrestle the remote control away from his son.

TIP...
Think: what do my words and actions really teach my children?

If Dad insists on turning the TV off immediately, it's highly likely that he and Brandon are going to physically hurt each other. Putting a twist on an old cliché, Dad is likely to win the fight, but lose the war. Dad can get the TV off, but look what he's teaching Brandon in the long run:

1. Education is important; important enough that I'm going to fight you to get you to do your homework.

2. If I can't get you to do what I tell you to do, I'll force you to do it.

3. The stronger person wins the battle.

4. It's okay to strike people in this family when you get mad.

Now, the first lesson is an important one: Education is important. But are there more humane and effective ways to get that message across to kids? Yes.

The next three lessons can be disastrous messages for children, especially if repeated over time. Children learn to solve their problems by fighting. They learn that it's all right to hit family members to get their way. And they miss out on learning many valuable lessons about how to solve disagreements.

With these points in mind, we believe that it's better to let the child watch TV rather than physically fight with him. Parents can use the TV as part of the consequence; the child can lose TV for a day, a couple of days, or a week, depending on how often this is a problem. If the problem persists, consider removing the TV altogether. This will send a clear message about the importance of education and following instructions!

EXAMPLE 5

Adam, 16, was out drinking with his friends last night. It is now the next morning and Dad is about to talk with Adam about drinking. Dad starts with Corrective Teaching but then switches to Teaching Self-Control when Adam yells and swears.

Corrective Teaching

 Stop the problem behavior.

Dad: "Adam, come here. I want to talk to you."

Adam: "I know what you're going to say. I'm sorry about what happened last night. And it won't happen again."

Dad: "Good, I'm glad you understand that drinking at your age is wrong."

 Give a consequence.

Dad: "Now, your consequence is to stay around the house for a week with no friends and no weekend activities."

Adam: "Dad, I just told you I was sorry about what happened last night. I make one lousy mistake, and you come down on me like the police!"

Teaching Self-Control, Part One: Calming Down

 Describe the problem behavior.

Dad: "Hey son, I know this is hard, but you've got to calm down so we can discuss it."

Adam: "You don't want to discuss anything. You just want to ruin my life. You know I was going camping this weekend with Jim and you ruined it."

Dad: "Adam, stop it. You're yelling."

Adam: "You're !*#@! right I'm yelling..."

Dad: "...and getting yourself upset."

 Give clear instructions.

Dad: "Now you can sit here or go to your room and calm down."

Adam: "I'm not going to my room!"

Dad: "I'll be happy to discuss this with you."

Adam: "I'm tired of this !*#@! All right!!"

Allow time to calm down.

Dad: "Now we're not going to get anywhere if we're both upset. I'll talk to you about this later." *(Dad leaves room to give both of them time to calm down.)*

Part Two: Follow-Up Teaching

 Describe what your child could do differently next time.

Dad: "Can we try it again? I know it's hard, but you can't yell and argue when you're given a consequence."

Adam: "I said I was sorry."

Dad: "I'm glad. I hope it doesn't happen again. But when you're given a consequence, if you can just accept it and discuss it calmly, it's a sign of maturity. And you save yourself a lot of trouble."

Adam: "Yeah, yeah, I know."

 Practice what your child can do next time.

Dad: "Now, your consequence is you're around the house for a week and you're not going camping with Jim."

Adam: "Whatever."

 Give a consequence.

Dad: "And because it took so long to settle this, you can help me by cleaning out the garage."

EXAMPLE 6

Brooke, 14, wants to go to the mall with her friends. She asks her father for permission. Dad tells Brooke that she has to clean her room first, then she can go to the mall. Brooke argues and complains about having to clean her room. Dad uses Teaching Self-Control in response to Brooke's arguing.

Corrective Teaching

 Stop the problem behavior.

Brooke: "I really need new shoes. Can I go shopping with my friends?"

Dad: "Brooke, remember we said you couldn't go shopping until your room is clean."

Brooke: "Can't that wait until later? I really need new shoes and all my friends are going today."

Dad: "No, Brooke, you've been putting this off for weeks. Your room's a pit. Now, you're not going shopping until that room is cleaned!"

Brooke: "I hate you! Why is cleaning my room so important anyway?"

Dad: *(Upset, but keeping anger in check)* "Now, you're yelling at me young lady."

Brooke: "No, duh."

Dad: "I didn't say that you couldn't go shopping, period. I said you couldn't go until your room was clean."

Brooke: "That is still unfair! Why is everything that you want always more important than me?"

2 Give a consequence.

Dad: "You're still yelling and for yelling, you won't be able to go shopping with your friends today. Just calm down."

Teaching Self-Control, Part One: Calming Down

1 Describe the problem behavior.

Brooke: "Why? Just give me one good reason why I can't go!!!"

Dad: "Because you're still yelling and because your room is not clean."

Brooke: "So... ."

2 Give clear instructions.

Dad: "Now, you need to calm down. You can either sit here and calm down or you can go to your room and calm down, but you must calm down."

3 Allow time to calm down.

Brooke: *(As Dad is walking out of the room)* "That's your answer to everything! 'Calm down and we'll talk about it later.' What a jerk!"

Brooke goes to her room. After 15 minutes, Dad goes in to see if she's ready to discuss the problem. Brooke is wearing headphones and listening to music.

Dad: "Are you ready to talk about this now?"

Brooke: *(Brooke ignores her dad.)*

Dad: *(Dad turns off the stereo.)* "Are you ready?"

Brooke: "What did you do that for?"

Dad: "So we could talk."

Brooke: "Go talk to yourself."

Dad: "I'll be back later." *(Dad leaves the room.)*

Brooke: "Don't bother."

Part Two: Follow-Up Teaching

 4 Describe what your child could do differently next time.

Dad: (Dad walks back into Brooke's room.) "You look like you've calmed down. You want to talk about this now so you can get on with your day?"

Brooke: "I guess so, but I still don't think this is fair. I can clean my room anytime."

Dad: "Look, I know you wanted to go shopping with your friends, but you can't yell at me every time you want your way."

Brooke: "How are you supposed to know I'm mad?"

Dad: "That's the point – you can take some deep breaths and take a break. And just discuss with me about the fact that you disagree. If you do that, then you keep yourself out of trouble. All right?"

Brooke: "I guess so, but I really wanted to go shopping with my friends."

Dad: "I know you did. But sometimes you can't do everything you want. Okay?"

5 Practice what your child can do next time.

Dad: "Show me how you're going to talk to me the next time you get angry with me because I don't let you go with your friends."

Brooke: "I guess I'd say, 'Dad, I need a chance to think about this. I really don't think this is fair.'"

Dad: "That's much better. You stayed calm. You took a break. And you didn't argue. You'll have fewer problems, you'll be with your friends sooner. And you and I won't have this kind of trouble. Okay?"

Brooke: "Can I go with my friends now?"

6 Give a consequence.

Dad: "Like I said before, you yelled at me so you won't be going with your friends today. And there's some things I want you to help me with around the house."

Brooke: (Brooke is upset again.) "This is so unfair."

Dad: "Now, wait a second. Stop and think before you say anything more. Now, if you need to take a break, this is the time to ask for it."

Brooke: "I need a break."

Dad: "Yes, that's much better."

Helpful Hints

➤ **Stay on task**. Don't lose sight of what you're trying to teach. Your children may try to argue with what you say or call you names. They may say you don't love them or accuse you of being unfair. Expect these statements but don't respond to them. If you find yourself responding to what your child is saying, remember to use a key phrase – "We'll talk about that when you calm down."

TIP... Encourage your children to talk with you about their feelings.

➤ **Be aware of your physical actions.** These times can be emotionally explosive. You don't want to encourage any physical retaliation from your child and you don't want to be seen as a threat. Some parents find that sitting helps calm the situation quickly. When parents stand up – particularly fathers – they tend to be more threatening. Any action viewed as aggressive, such as pointing your index finger, leaning over your child, or raising a fist, will only make matters worse and make it less likely that your child will calm down.

➤ **Plan consequences in advance.** Think of appropriate negative consequences beforehand, especially if losing self-control is a problem for your child.

Find time when your child is not upset to explain to her what the consequence will be the next time she argues and fights with you. For example, "Sarah, when I tell you 'No' sometimes you want to argue with me. Then you get mad and start yelling. From now on, if you do this, you will lose your phone privileges for two nights." Then use Preventive Teaching to help Sarah learn how to accept decisions.

➤ **Follow up.** As your child calms down and you complete the teaching sequence, side issues can arise. For example, some situations may call for a problem-solving approach. Your child may not have the knowledge or experience to deal with a certain situation. It may be very beneficial to take the time to help find solutions.

Other situations may call for a firm, emphatic ending to Teaching Self-Control. You may want to indicate that the child's behavior is clearly unacceptable and that the interaction is finished: "Okay, we've practiced what to do. Now, go to your brother's room and apologize to him."

Still other situations may call for an understanding approach. Some kids cry after an intense situation. They just don't know how to handle what they're feeling inside. Then you can say, "Let's sit down and talk about why you've been feeling so angry. Maybe I can help. At least, I can listen." Whatever approach you take will be determined by your common sense and judgment.

Earlier we mentioned that you shouldn't get sidetracked with all of the comments and issues that kids may bring up when they are angry. But that's only during the Teaching Self-Control process. It is important, after everyone's calmed down, to follow up on those statements that upset or concerned you. This is when you can find out the reasons behind the outburst. Talk about trust. Ask your child to share feelings and opinions with you in ways that will help, not hurt, everyone in the family.

Whenever possible, implement the suggestions your children make. By doing so, you will be opening the door to more constructive conversations with your children. Frequently, going through these rough times together forms the tightest emotional bonds between you and your kids.

Questions and Comments from Parents

Q. If my kid gets upset when I ask him to clean his room and make his bed, does the consequence involve not making his bed or the tantrum that follows?

A. When you ask your child to make his bed and he has a tantrum, use Teaching Self-Control to give the child a chance to calm down. Use the Follow-Up Teaching steps to teach the child ways to remain calm and give a consequence for the tantrum.

Q. What if I send my child to her room to calm down and she sits in her room all night?

A. Children have chosen to stay in their rooms all night in some situations. Check on your child regularly to make sure she's okay. If she decides she doesn't want to work it out before she goes to sleep for the night, then leave her in bed and try to do the Follow-Up Teaching the next morning. Sometimes, a good night's sleep is helpful for everyone in that situation. The important thing is to make sure you come back to the situation the next day. Otherwise, your child learns to avoid dealing with the problem by hanging out in her room.

Q. What should my child do when I give him time to calm down and use one of the options I suggested?

A. The child should be doing whatever helps him calm down. Some suggestions include listening to music, taking deep breaths, counting to 100, writing in a diary, or going for a walk. One mother let her son do physical exercise to help him calm down. He would lift weights or shoot baskets in the driveway. Sometimes that's not possible, so teach your children a variety of ways to calm down.

It is really helpful to work out a "staying calm plan" with your child and use Preventive Teaching before blow-ups or intense problems occur.

Q. Why should I start with praise if my child just swore at me?

A. It probably won't be helpful to start with praise if your child is swearing at you. Instead, try starting with empathy. Empathy is a statement that shows you understand how he is feeling. For example, you might say, "I know you're upset about not being able to go to your friend's house, but stop the yelling and swearing and calm down. I'll be back in a few minutes to talk with you."

Q. What should I be doing during the time my child is calming down?

A. If you are upset, this is the time to use your "staying calm plan." It is also helpful to plan your next steps for dealing with your child. You can practice the Follow-Up Teaching, and decide on a consequence.

Q. What good does it do to let my kid go off by himself after he has misbehaved?

A. Sometimes people need to be alone to think about what they're saying and doing; staying around the people they are arguing with adds to the problem. When you give your child and yourself time alone, you're both more likely to calm down and think about what to do rather than reacting negatively to everything each one of you is saying. Giving your child an opportunity to truly calm down can shorten the duration of the problem behavior. Once you're both calm, you can focus on attacking the problem and not each other.

Q. What if this happens in the morning when I have to get to work and my kid has to get to school?

A. You have two choices. Either send the child to school and tell her that you'll finish when you both get home. Or call school and work to let them know you'll be late and take care of the situation before you leave.

Q. **What if I do get real angry and strike my child?**

A. First, check to make sure that you haven't physically hurt your child. If you have hurt him or her, then get proper medical care. Next, figure out what made you angry enough to strike your child and make a plan to take a break before you get that angry when you are in those situations. You will also want to apologize to your child. Finally, you may want to talk to a counselor for additional suggestions about staying calm when you're angry. Or call the Boys Town National Hotline at 1-800-448-3000 and talk with one of the counselors about help in your community. Counselors are available 24 hours a day, seven days a week to help you or your children.

Q. **What if my child gets angry and strikes me or someone else?**

A. Take a break away from your child. Don't corner or aggressively approach him; he may do something else that harms you or him. Check to make sure you're physically okay. If you need medical attention, make sure your child is safe or with another trusted adult before going for medical aid.

If medical aid is not necessary, then make sure that you and your child take time to calm down. There is no need to rush into giving a consequence right now. Remember that your child will eventually get a consequence for the misbehavior when you do the Follow-Up Teaching after he is calm.

Try to determine what caused the problem. Then use Preventive Teaching to teach your child how to deal with the situation without striking others. Most likely, you will want to teach him how to share his feelings verbally rather than acting them out physically. It may take several months of patience and consistent teaching before your child stops hitting. But in the long run, you are helping him learn nonaggressive ways to work out future problems in situations when he gets upset.

Q. **Is it okay to use spanking?**

A. These days, there are many arguments about whether parents should spank their children. At Boys Town, we do not recommend spanking or hitting children with other objects. Spanking has potentially negative side effects that can generally be avoided with other types of negative consequences. Read Chapter 1 again for examples of other consequences that work better than spanking and don't have the negative effects.

Q. **How are my children going to hear what I am saying if they are yelling and screaming?**

A. Children often copy what they see their parents doing. So if they're yelling, the best thing for you to do is to stay quiet and calm. This may be difficult, but your children are more likely to calm down if you're calm. When you're yelling, they're more likely to feel like they have to yell to get heard. When you're quiet, they can express their ideas in a normal voice tone.

Q. **My child starts to destroy our house (lamps, furniture, windows) when he gets angry. HELP! What can I do? (I'm not a millionaire.)**

A. If your child gets too destructive, you may want to call for some help – a respected family member, a support person, or the police. It should be someone the child will listen to and who can convince the child to stop the behavior.

Q. **My kids would never respond like the kids in the video.**

A. It may seem like the kids in the video calm down much quicker than your own children. We produced these videos to show you the steps, so you may not hear these exact words or have the same experiences in your home. But the steps do work; you just need to keep using them.

Q. What if my child wants to go smoke a cigarette to calm down?

A. We don't recommend allowing children to smoke under any circumstances. It's bad for their health and against the law for them to purchase cigarettes. Nevertheless, some parents choose to let their children smoke or feel that smoking is less problematic than other things their children could be doing.

   If you allow your children to smoke at other times, then letting them smoke to calm down is probably an option you can choose. If you don't let them smoke at other times, then don't let them start just to help them calm down. Deep breathing will produce similar calming effects.

Q. How long does Teaching Self-Control take? It looks like it could take awhile.

A. The time to calm down is the longest part of Teaching Self-Control. It could last anywhere from 10 minutes to a couple of days. In either case, make sure you wait until the child is calm before starting Follow-Up Teaching.

Q. How do I know when my child is calmed down?

A. When your child is calm, she will be willing to follow some simple instructions that you give. For example, you could say, "Let's go to the kitchen to talk" or "Why don't you sit up here." If she follows your instructions, you can probably do Follow-Up Teaching. If she doesn't follow instructions, she is probably not calm yet and you may need to give her more time to calm down.

Exercise 1 – Making a Plan for Staying Calm

Complete the blanks to make a plan to stay calm in intense situations.

Step 1. What do my children do that really upsets me?

_____

_____

_____

_____

Step 2. What are my early warning signals that tell me that I am getting upset?

_____

_____

_____

_____

Step 3. What can I do to stay calm?

_____

_____

_____

_____

Staying Calm Plan

When my child and I feel _____

_____

and I feel _____

_____

_____

I will _____

_____

_____

Homework 1 – Teaching Self-Control

Please write down one situation involving Teaching Self-Control that occurred with your child. Write down what you did for each step of Teaching Self-Control.

Situation:_____

1. Describe the problem behavior. _____
   _____

2. Give clear instructions. _____
   _____

3. Allow time to calm down. _____
   _____

4. Describe what your child could do differently next time._____
   _____

5. Practice what your child can do next time._____
   _____

6. Give a consequence. _____
   _____

What was the result? _____
_____
_____

Is there anything you would do differently if this situation occurred again? _____
_____
_____
_____

CHAPTER 6

Helping Children Succeed in School

Children spend almost half of their waking hours in school or school-related activities. Studies have shown that children whose parents are involved in their education do better than those children whose parents are not involved.

In this chapter, we'll learn about:

➤ Home activities that will help your children do well in school.

➤ Ways parents can communicate with teachers, counselors, and school administrators.

Home Activities that Can Help Your Child in School

Many of the problems that kids experience at school are related to their behavior rather than their academic abilities. For example, many children who do poorly in school often don't do homework or are disruptive in class.

On the other hand, some of the most academically successful students are the ones who also behave well in class. They follow instructions, accept criticism, and get along with their classmates. Students who are socially competent have a better chance of doing well academically.

School Social Skills

Here's a list of social skills that will help your child in school.

1. How to follow instructions
2. How to say "No" to friends
3. How to accept "No" answers
4. How to ask permission
5. How to apologize
6. How to disagree appropriately
7. How to stay calm
8. How to accept a consequence or criticism
9. How to get along with others
10. How to let parents/teachers know where you're going
11. How to ask for help
12. How to dress appropriately
13. How to complete homework
14. How to join in a conversation
15. How to ask questions
16. How to manage time
17. How to be prepared for class
18. How to stay on task
19. How to be on time
20. How to get the teacher's attention
21. How to ignore distractions by others
22. How to contribute to group activities
23. How to study
24. How to wait your turn
25. How to volunteer to help
26. How to express pride in accomplishments

Specific information about each of these skills is in Appendix B.

Here are three things that you can do at home that will help your children's school behavior and academic performance.

1. Teach your children social skills, that is, how to get along with teachers and classmates.
2. Get involved in your children's education.
3. Schedule time each day for homework.

Teach Your Children Social Skills

One of the first things you can do is to make sure that your child can (and will) follow instructions. Children literally get hundreds of instructions each day in school; "Take out your books and open them to Chapter 12", "Pass your papers to your right", "Be sure to complete the odd-numbered problems and bring them to class tomorrow." If your children have difficulty responding to these reasonable requests then, they will have difficulty with the school work as well.

Additionally, your children will be able to do well in school if you teach them how to accept criticism, ask permission, and ask for help. Each of these skills will help them get more out of classroom instruction and homework. The skill, "how to ask for help" is especially important and often difficult for children. When you teach your children how to ask for help before they talk with the teacher, they'll be much more likely to feel comfortable in the actual situation. Watch "Session Three, Preventing Misbehaviors" again if you would like more information about teaching social skills to children.

Get Involved in Your Children's Education

Studies have shown that parental involvement in school goes hand-in-hand with children's success in school. There are many ways to get involved in your children's education. You can volunteer at school, attend school activities, and spend time focusing on school when your children are at home. School involvement also includes such things as helping your child with homework and frequent communication with your child's teachers. We'll cover both of these topics in detail later in this chapter.

Asking your children about their school day is a great way to get involved with their education. However, getting kids to share information about school activities can be a challenge.

Often, children respond with one-word answers when parents ask about school. A question such as, "How was school today?" usually gets an answer like "Fine" or "Boring." Questions such as, "What did you learn today?" usually get "Nothing" for a response.

If you ask your children to actually show you or tell you something specific about their school day, you're more likely to get full-sentence answers. For example, ask for information by saying, "Show me what you did in social studies today" or "Tell me about your math test today" or "What did you play at recess? Who else played?"

Additionally, when you ask questions about school that you know your children enjoy, you open the door to discussing other school topics. For example, ask your children for an update on classmates or friends, what they had for lunch, or which teachers they like best. Questions about topics they're interested in eventually can lead to questions about topics that let you know how they're doing academically in school.

Schedule Time Each Day for Homework

Completing homework helps children learn and retain new information. Homework also helps children improve their understanding of class material and enhances academic performance.

Starting a study time routine in your home

If your children are just starting school or are in the early elementary grades, then except for some minor moans and groans, you should have little trouble establishing a regular study time. On the other hand, if you have junior high students or teenagers, and you haven't had a regular study time, then expect some major resistance to this new idea. In either case, stick with the routine through the mumbling and grumbling. In the long run, your children will be the ones who benefit from getting a study time routine started in your home.

➤ **Establish one central location for completing homework.** Make sure the place has a clean working surface (a kitchen table or a desk in your child's room).

➤ **Keep the area as quiet as possible for study time.** Shut off the TV and radio. Keep younger children occupied by reading them a story or having them play outside while their older sister or brother is studying.

Study Time Activities

Here are some other activities for children who say they have no homework to do during study time.

- Read aloud to you or a younger brother or sister.

- Read a newspaper article about world events, nutrition, teen issues, or any other interesting topic.

- Watch the news and talk with you about current events.

- Write letters to friends, grandparents, or relatives.

- Cut coupons and add up the amount of money saved.

- Write in a journal or diary.

- Put together a puzzle.

- Use educational software on a computer.

- Write a list of things they can do to help at home, in the neighborhood, or in the community.

- Draw a picture of their family, home, or community.

- Prepare a budget for their expenses as if they were living on their own.

- Help you prepare dinner. Emphasize measuring and counting skills.

- Make greeting cards (for example, birthday or Christmas cards) for family members.

- Build things using household objects; for example, paper, popsicle sticks, milk cartons, and paper plates.

➤ **Set a specific amount of study time for each school night.** For children in the elementary grades, recommended study time is 30 to 45 minutes; for junior high students, 45 to 75 minutes; and for high school students, 60 to 90 minutes or more.

➤ **Divide study time into smaller periods for children who have difficulty concentrating for long periods of time.** Some children, especially younger ones, may do better if they study for 15 minutes, take a short break, then study for another 15 minutes. It also may be helpful for parents just beginning a study time routine to start with smaller amounts of time for homework. Then, after two weeks of the routine, add time to the schedule. Continue adding time every two weeks until your children reach the recommended amounts of time for their age group or ability.

➤ **Schedule the study time so that it best fits your family's routines.** For some children, right after school is a good time for homework. However, for parents who work outside the home, it often is tough to monitor and help with homework right after school. A time in the early evening when you and they still have some energy works best for many families. Then, if assignments take longer than expected, they can get the homework completed without staying up so late. You also can avoid some of the frustration and fighting that sometimes occurs when fatigue sets in and homework piles up.

➤ **Have children study for a set amount of time even if they don't have assigned homework.** If children don't bring assignments home, or they tell you they completed all their homework in school, they can always do projects for extra credit, or read books, magazines, or newspapers. The goal is to have them learning.

➤ **Have your children do their homework first,** before they use privileges like watching TV, talking on the phone, or going to a friend's house.

➤ **Use Preventive Teaching to set expectations for study time.** It's not unusual for children to resist changes in study time, especially if they have not had to study much in the past. Preventive Teaching gives you an easy approach for explaining your expectations to the children. First, tell them what you expect. Second, give them a reason for the changes. And third, have them practice the new study routine right away.

➤ **Start small and build slowly.** Your goal is to build good study habits over time. If you have not previously had a scheduled study time, you can introduce study time all at once; for example, explain your study time routine on Sunday afternoon and start the routine that night. Or you can introduce study time gradually, adding another part each week or two as suggested in the example below.

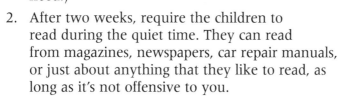

1. Set up a nightly 30-minute quiet time. Don't expect children to study yet. Just let them know that there will be a time each night when the radio and television are off. (Also start making sure that your children are bringing home the books or assignments they need.)

2. After two weeks, require the children to read during the quiet time. They can read from magazines, newspapers, car repair manuals, or just about anything that they like to read, as long as it's not offensive to you.

3. After two weeks of reading, require that schoolbooks be present during the reading and quiet time. The children don't have to read the schoolbooks; the books just have to be there on the table.

4. After the books show up consistently, require the children to read from schoolbooks for half the quiet time and from other materials for the remaining time.

5. Finally, gradually increase the amount of time children spend studying until all assignments are getting completed.

Keep in mind that it may take awhile to get study time running smoothly. There might be some slipping along the way, but if you stick with the schedule and continue to give encouragement for completing each improvement, you're likely to see positive results at home and at school.

Helping with homework

It is not unusual for children to have difficulty with their assignments. And while teachers have a variety of approaches for helping students, parents are typically the ones who are around when homework gets completed. So let's start with some ideas for getting through those assignments.

> **TIP...**
> Teach children how to ask for help before they get behind in their schoolwork.

Set a positive example. Keep the TV off and read a book, write a letter, balance the checkbook, or make a grocery list while the kids are studying.

Be available. Watch for opportunities to praise them for staying on task with their homework. Make sure your children have the necessary materials for homework, such as a notebook for keeping track of assignments. Check to see that they are bringing books or other supplies home that they'll need to complete their homework. Then, be sure that they start studying at the designated time each day.

Help your children organize their time so that they can fit homework into their schedule. Some children are so busy with extra activities and jobs that homework just doesn't fit into their day. Help these youngsters reorganize their schedule and, when necessary, drop some of those extra activities or work fewer hours on the job so they can make homework a priority.

Use a chart or contract to keep track of and reward your child's homework completion. Students typically receive grades once a semester or after major tests. This doesn't always give students the frequent feedback they need to stick with a homework routine. Charts and contracts give parents and kids immediate feedback about their homework completion on a daily basis. Chapter 2 includes samples of charts and contracts that parents can adapt to help children with homework.

Helping when you know the subject matter

If you know the material, then ask your children questions that lead them to the answer. Avoid doing the assignment or finding the answer for them. Instead, help them find the answer so that over time, they'll learn how to discover answers on their own.

For example, if your son comes across a word he doesn't know, help him look it up in the dictionary, even if you know what the word means. While he might groan about having to use the dictionary, he's learning how to find definitions of unknown words, a valuable skill for his future.

Or, if your daughter has trouble with an algebra equation, you can ask her to review material in her math book, ask her what the different parts of the equation mean, or ask her to describe what she knows about the problem. Each question may lead your daughter toward the correct answer and to a better understanding of the process for solving algebra problems in the future.

Helping when you don't know the subject matter

Okay, so maybe there will be times when you don't feel comfortable helping with fractions or physics or diagramming sentences. There are still some things you can do to help your children complete their assignments.

➤ Teach your children how to ask the teacher for extra help by asking questions before, during, or after class. Asking for help is an important skill for children to learn. Some children feel uncomfortable asking questions, even when the teacher encourages questions from students. So, use Preventive Teaching to teach your children how to ask for help before they get dangerously behind on assignments they don't understand.

➤ Ask the teacher or school counselor to recommend a student tutor for your child. Often, both the tutor and your child benefit from the tutoring sessions. Plus, some children feel more comfortable getting help from a peer rather than from an adult.

➤ If there's an older child at home who is able to help, have him or her work with the younger child to get assignments completed. Older children can help with spelling and reading, reviewing flash cards for math facts, or completing various writing assignments. Be sure to monitor the help the older child is providing so that he or she doesn't do the assignments for younger siblings. In addition to getting homework completed, having siblings help each other builds strong relationships between the children.

➤ Have your child call a homework help line. Check with your school district's office about the availability of a help line for your children.

These are just some of the ideas that parents have shared with us over the years. See which approach works best with your child. If homework and grades don't improve, try another method. Ask the teacher or school counselor for suggestions and support for you and your child. Both the teacher and counselor probably are responsible for a large number of students, so stick with the phone calls and visits to school. Your child's education depends on it.

Communicating with Teachers and School Administrators

In our work with schools and parents, it's not unusual to find teachers who blame parents for the problems they see in the classroom. Nor is it unusual to find parents who blame teachers for the problems their children are having at school. If we are going to help children get the best possible education, parents and teachers need to work together, rather than against each other. While both parents and teachers can do things that will encourage good relationships with each other, we're going to focus on what parents can do to build strong relationships with teachers.

Attend school activities.

Attend the open house that almost every school offers at the beginning of the school year and meet with your children's teachers.

Some parents feel intimidated or uncomfortable about meeting with teachers. That's understandable, especially if they had difficulties of their own when they were in school. As one mother put it, "I thought 9th grade was hard the first time, it's twice as hard this second time!" If that's the case with you, then you might have to force yourself to attend the meetings. Remember, your effort now pays off big for your children later. So do whatever you must to get yourself to the meetings. Before the meeting, write questions to ask teachers. Then make yourself ask at least one question with each of your children's teachers. There's a list of questions to get you started on page 129.

Communicate when things go well.

One way you can build strong relationships with your children's teachers is to call, write a note, or stop by the school to say something nice to the teacher. Pick out something that your child likes about the teacher or class. It can be related to games they play at recess, extra help with math, where your child sits in class, activities on the computer, or an opportunity to read a report to the class. Then share that with the teacher. It may be even more helpful to share that good news with the principal, too! You're going to make that teacher's day! Just think of how you feel when you hear something good about yourself or your kids.

TIP...
Let teachers know what your children like about their classes.

Share problems when they're small.

When there is a problem, call the teacher and ask how your child is doing instead of waiting for the teacher to call you. It's especially important to take care of problems when they're small. Get help early in the process and you have the best chance of finding a solution and avoiding major problems. Listed below are some guidelines for working with teachers and school staff to help solve school problems.

Working with Your Child's Teachers to Solve School Problems

Parents often get nervous when called to school because of a problem. Here are four steps that parents have used when they find themselves in this type of situation.

1. Stay calm.
2. Get information.
3. Take care of the problem.
4. Prevent future problems.

 Stay calm.

When you get a call from school, you may be busy at work, taking care of three other children, in the middle of an argument with your spouse, or just heading out the door with a list of things to do. These calls always seem to come at the worst time. But is there ever really a good time to get a call from school? Anyone with children has a full plate, night or day.

It's natural to feel upset when you get a call from school. But if you can stay calm, you are much more likely to help your child resolve the problem.

What can you do to stay calm in this situation? Do you remember your plan for staying calm? Can you use some of those same techniques here? If you're feeling upset, take a few deep breaths and try to relax. Or take a minute after you get the call to talk with a friend or relative

Questions for Teachers

Not sure what to ask teachers at school meetings? Here's a list of possible questions.

- "Where does my son sit?"

- "What does this test mean?"

- "Do all the assignments have to be typed?"

- "How can my daughter get her assignments typed if I don't have a computer or typewriter?"

- "How much homework do you give?"

- "About how much time should my son be spending on his homework?"

- "Who can I call if my daughter needs help with her homework and I don't know how to help her?"

- "Can my son come to school early if he needs extra help understanding his school work?"

- "When is a good time to call you if I need to ask you something about my child?"

This last question is especially important. So, while meeting with the teachers, find out when you can call them if you have questions. Also, explain to them that you want them to call you whenever you can be of help.

about the problem. This will give you time to calm down and get prepared to discuss solutions to the problem. If you think it would help, ask the friend or relative to go to the school with you.

 Get information.

When you get to the school, ask specific questions so that you understand the problem. Your goal is not to challenge whether there is a problem, but to get specific information. Be sure to find out what happened and how your child was involved. The following types of questions may be helpful.

Who was involved in the problem?

What were they doing?

Where did the problem happen?

When did this happen?

How did this happen?

Keep in mind that the school administration may be trying to get your child to answer these same questions. Encourage your child to cooperate and work with the school personnel as they try to get a complete picture of the problem.

Don't take sides or defend your child's behavior. Remember, the goal of the meeting with your child's teacher or school administrator is to get information, solve the immediate problem, and look for ways to help your child do better in the future. Try your best, and have your child try his or her best, to cooperate and work with the school.

Take care of the problem.

Ask the teachers or administrators if they have any suggestions for solving the problem or improving the situation. They work with a variety of children and may have effective ways for constructively responding to this particular problem.

Offer your suggestions for solving the problem or improving the situation. Trust your instincts; no one knows your child as well as you do. Share your opinion about the proposed solution, but be open to new ideas from the school staff.

When a decision is made, work to put it into place. For example, if your child is suspended, then get a list of assignments or other schoolwork that he or she can do at home. Often, readmission to school is based on time and completion of school work. If the solution involves apologies to teachers or classmates, use Preventive Teaching to prepare your child for those events.

At the conclusion of the meeting, thank the school staff for their time and concern. Calling a parent to the school is typically stressful for everyone involved. Let the staff know that you appreciate their efforts on behalf of your child.

Prevent future problems.

Work with your child to keep the problem from happening again. If homework completion is a problem, then set up a nightly study time and check homework every night to make sure it is completed.

If behavior in class is the problem, then set up some way to communicate with your child's teacher as often as necessary. (In the next section, we discuss school notes, an effective way to have frequent contact with teachers.)

Additionally, use Preventive Teaching to teach skills that your child can use to successfully handle situations that have posed a problem in the past. Talk to your child about possible solutions that will prevent problems from occurring in the future.

For example, If your daughter doesn't understand a biology assignment and it's keeping her from getting homework turned in, then:

➤ teach her how to ask for help,

➤ see if there's any classmate who can tutor her, and

➤ check to see if your school has a homework help line.

If your son is getting into fights, then teach him:

➤ how to walk away from angry peers,

➤ how to take a deep breath and keep his cool,

➤ how to solve problems through negotiation and compromise, and

➤ how to recognize and avoid situations that might lead to fights.

TIP... Frequent communication with teachers helps prevent problems.

When possible, get your children's input into the solution. The more input they have, the more likely they are to follow through with the solution.

Finally, communicate with your child's teachers more frequently so that you are finding out about problems before they become major issues.

Using School Notes to Monitor Your Child's Progress

One way to increase communication with teachers is through school notes. We usually use school notes when a student is having problems and regular contact between parents and teachers is necessary. School notes also can be used to communicate things your child is doing well. Studies have shown that students whose parents give positive and negative consequences based on school notes have better behavior and grades in school.

School notes can be informal or formal. Informal notes are generally brief, handwritten messages. Your child's teacher might write, "Michael did well in spelling today" or "Please ask Michael to tell you about the problem in recess today." You might write to the teacher, "Michael had trouble with his homework. I helped him with the math but we weren't able to get problem 25 worked out" or "I talked with Michael about hitting classmates at recess. We discussed how to get what he wants by asking rather than hitting. Please let me know how he does today. Thanks for all your patience with him."

Formal school notes can include a list of the child's classes and space for the teacher's comments on how the child is doing in class or with homework. Students carry the school note with them to each class and use it with each teacher with whom there is a problem. Teachers complete the note at the end of the class or school day and send it home with the child. You review the note with your child at home and provide praise and privileges for positive school behavior or correction and loss of privileges for problem behavior.

Here are two examples of school notes. Adapt them to work for you and your child.

This first example is for younger children or children who only have one teacher each day. The teacher circles "y" or "n" each day to let the parent know whether Michael stayed in his seat, followed directions, or turned in his homework. Michael brings this card home daily, or, if he is doing well consistently, the card goes home once per week. Parents then provide additional privileges for "y's" and fewer privileges for "n's." We would encourage parents to use a contract or chart along with a school note so children and parents know what privileges are available depending on how children do in school.

> **TIP...**
> Use formal and informal school notes to improve communication between home and school.

Dear Mrs. Miller,

    We're trying to help Michael do better in school. Please check "Yes" or "No" for each behavior. Then initial and send this note home with Michael each day. Thanks.

Mrs. Johnson

	M	T	W	T	F
1. Stays in seat	y/n	y/n	y/n	y/n	y/n
2. Follows directions	y/n	y/n	y/n	y/n	y/n
3. Turns in homework	y/n	y/n	y/n	y/n	y/n
Initials	___	___	___	___	___

This second school note is for older children or children who have several teachers during their school day. Each teacher checks whether Michael was on time, completed homework, and followed instructions. The teacher also initials the note to show that the teacher, not the student, completed the school note. Like the first note, parents provide privileges depending on the number of periods where Michael was on time, finished homework, and followed instructions. While parents and teachers use this particular note for just one day, you could design a school note for teachers to use across several days.

Teachers,

We are trying to help Michael do better in all of his classes. Please note whether Michael did these things during this past week and then initial. Please call us at 555-1070 if you have any questions.

Period	In Class on Time	Homework Completed	Followed Instructions	Teacher's Initials
1				
2				
3				
4				
5				
6				
7				
8				

It helps to keep school note information brief and specific. Make it easy for teachers to quickly circle the positive or negative behaviors listed on the note. Ask teachers to call you if they need to give you more detailed information.

Review the school note at home.

The school note is most helpful when parents and teachers use it regularly and pay attention to the information on the note. If you and your child's teacher have agreed to use the note for daily communication, then review it each day as soon as you and your child can do so. If the teacher completes the note weekly, then review it at the end of each week. Here are some key points to remember when reviewing your child's school note.

School Transitions

School is a series of changes for your children. They move from preschool to elementary to junior high to high school, and then on to a job, vocational school, or college. Each year children must make the transition from summer play to structured school rooms. Every school day, they go from one subject or classroom to another.

Here are some hints that parents have shared with us for helping children through these transitions.

- Be positive about school. Talk with your kids about the good things that happen there. Tell them about some of your good experiences with school.

- Start talking about school as early in a child's life as possible. Set the expectation that your child will get a good education.

- Expect your child to experience some stress related to school, tests, friends, and homework. Be understanding when they tell you about frustrations. Then, help them figure out how to fix the problem or deal with the frustration. This way, they can learn from their experiences and be successful in these situations in the future.

- Listen to your kids and what they tell you about school. Sometimes it just helps to let them talk about what's going on in their lives. Be supportive and attentive.

- Visit your children's school. Find out about the school day, the administration, and naturally, your children's teachers.

- Praise the good things that your children do. Especially focus on their successful attempts at solving problems with other children or in academic areas.

When your child brings the school note home, be sure to discuss the specific areas outlined by you or your child's teacher. Discuss whether there is improvement or backsliding in these areas.

Call the teacher if you need additional information.

Encourage your child's progress in the identified areas.

Use Effective Praise when your child accomplishes the daily or weekly goals. Provide the agreed-upon privileges or rewards when your child reaches the specified academic or behavioral goals.

Address problems immediately.

Use Corrective Teaching to help your child learn from problems at school. Follow through with negative consequences when your child doesn't behave well or complete school assignments.

Stop using the note.

Stop using the school note when your child consistently does well and the behavior problems are no longer a problem. We recommend that you gradually reduce use of the note. If your child has been carrying the note each day, then have the teacher summarize your child's behavior once or twice a week. If the note has been used weekly, then switch to every other week or arrange to talk on the phone with the teacher once a week without using a note.

Summary

Today's children are tomorrow's leaders. Who would you prefer leading our future: Children who are well-educated and can work through problems in constructive ways or children who missed out on an education because they wouldn't follow simple instructions or were too disruptive in class? The answer is obvious. And if our children are going to get that education, they'll do it best with the cooperation of parents and teachers.

Questions and Comments from Parents

Q. **How do I get my children to tell me about their school activities?**

A. Children are famous for one-word answers to questions about school and homework. Nevertheless, it is well worth parents' time and effort to talk with their children about school. Here are some things parents can do to improve communication about school with their kids.

First, find time each day to talk with your children about their activities. With hectic schedules, it's not easy to find time to spend with your kids. Parents have to look for every possible opportunity to stay involved in their children's and teens' lives. For example, use a ride to the movie, a trip to the store, jogging together, or a late night chat in their room to catch up on your kids' activities, friendships, worries, and interests.

Second, ask open-ended questions that generally get more than a one-word response. For example, "How was your day?" usually gets a "Fine", "Okay", or "All right" for a response. Next time try something like, "What did you think of your math test?" While they may not have liked the test, you're more likely to get a picture of how they did when you ask their opinion about the test.

Third, talk with your kids about other areas of their life as well as about school. Often, when you ask kids about what's important to them, for example, friends, music, likes, and dislikes, they're much more likely to share information about what may be more important to you, for example, school, homework, and grades.

Fourth, if you want kids to talk, you must be willing to listen. Take the opportunity to just listen without giving your opinion or the parental slant to their story. Pay attention to what they say – and what they don't say. For example, if they're talking about friends and one of their closest friends isn't mentioned in the conversation, it might help to ask about the friend. It might be nothing more than an oversight or it might be that the friend is doing things that he or she shouldn't and your child doesn't feel comfortable talking about the problem.

Finally, be patient. If you and your older child have not typically shared much time or information together, then don't expect your relationship to change overnight. Change takes time. Start with conversations about topics that won't lead to arguments. Over time, you can introduce topics on which you and your child disagree but, especially in the beginning, work to keep conversations focused on positive topics. This won't be easy, but remember that you are working on building a stronger relationship with your child. It's through that relationship that you can shape his willingness to discuss school activities and all the other events of his life.

Q. **How do I get my child to do her homework?**

A. We have included several sections on homework in this video and workbook. Reread this chapter and Chapter 2, "Encouraging Positive Behavior." In Chapter 2 the material on charts and contracts will help you and your daughter set goals for completing homework. In this chapter there are several suggestions for helping your child get started on homework. Establish a quiet time in your home and the expectation that homework will get completed during this time. Be consistent with your use of a quiet study time. This consistency, over time, will help your child understand the importance and benefit of homework completion.

Q. **What do I do if my teen skips school?**

A. Find out all you can about why he or she skipped school. Most reasons for skipping school are related to having fun. For example, in their mind they'll have more fun hanging out with friends or going to a movie than they will going to school. So, they skip school. Occasionally, kids skip school because they don't feel safe before, during, or after school. In those cases, talk with your child and your child's counselor to see what can be done to improve school safety for your child.

If your child skipped school because of an upcoming test, missing assignment, or to have fun with friends, then use Corrective Teaching to help your child understand that going to school is not a negotiable option. Typically, the child can be grounded for a week or more depending on how often this has been a problem in the past.

Most states require that children go to school until their 16th birthday. So, if your child has not yet reached that milestone, and he or she continually misses school, you can call the school counselor or truant officer to report that your child is not showing up for school. Get others involved to help you with the problem.

Q. **I can't help my child with her homework because I don't know enough about the subject matter. What should I do?**

A. We presented four possible answers for this question in this chapter. First, teach your child how to ask her teacher for additional help. Second, ask her teacher or school counselor to identify a student tutor for her. Third, ask an older brother or sister to help her, if possible. Fourth, have your daughter call a homework help line if there's one in your area.

A fifth possible approach would be for your child to teach you what she knows about the assignment. Have her go over prior material in the chapter or from her notes. Often, as she teaches you, she helps herself get a better understanding of how to complete her homework.

Keep in mind that when your child is asking for homework help, she is probably frustrated and may be upset. You are likely to hear complaints about the "stupid assignment" or "the teacher who doesn't know what he's doing." Now is not the time to debate teaching methods with your daughter. You want her to finish her assignment. So, let her know that you understand she's frustrated; for example, "It looks like you're upset about this." If you think it will help, let her take a short break (maybe 10 to 15 minutes). Then get her back on track as soon as possible with something such as, "Take a deep breath and tell me what you have to get finished for tomorrow." The more you know about the assignment, the more likely you can find her the help she needs.

Q. **If my child is suspended from school, what should he be doing all day?**

A. When your child is suspended, he typically will be given assignments that need to be completed before he is allowed back in class. Be sure to get books and assignments from the school so your child has work to do during regular school hours.

Once he has the materials, the challenge will be getting him to do the work. If you are employed during school hours, then monitoring his activities can be a problem. Look for support in this situation from all possible angles. Check with the school to see if they have any alternative settings for him to attend during the school day. See if the local Boys & Girls Club, church, or recreation center has anyone who could help. Without monitoring and supervision during the day, it is less likely that your son will stay out of trouble and complete the school work.

If you're at home during the day, then explain that you expect him to complete his school work. The TV and radio stay off. He can sit where you can see him, for example, at the kitchen table, while he does his work. Provide breaks during the day. Depending on his age and ability, breaks may occur every 15 to 60 minutes or so.

He will likely complain or try to avoid doing his work. Use the other skills such as Preventive Teaching and set up a chart or contract before study time starts. This can often prevent problems from occurring throughout the day. Also, use Corrective Teaching or Teaching Self-Control if problems arise.

Q. If my child is disciplined at school do I need to discipline her at home for the misbehavior?

A. If you ask your child, she'll probably say, "No. Why should I be punished twice for the same thing?!"

As a parent, the answer is not so straightforward. Each situation requires additional information and your judgment. As a general rule, for less serious problems or minor problems that occur infrequently, you probably don't need to give additional consequences at home. But for more serious problems or problems that are starting to occur frequently, an additional consequence may be necessary. Let's look at a couple of examples.

Your daughter has missed three math assignments so her teacher keeps her after school to complete the missing assignments. This consequence may be enough to help her to get her homework completed on time so another consequence at home may not be necessary. Then, to help prevent the problem in the future, you may want to have her show you her homework every night until she shows that she can get it completed on time.

Now, let's say that your daughter is caught drinking alcohol at a school function. As a result, she is suspended from the basketball team and not allowed at any school activities for one month. If you ground her for that month, you would be providing a negative consequence that supports the school's discipline. This consequence gives your daughter, her school, and her friends a clear message of how seriously you view her drinking.

Use your best judgment, talk with the teacher or principal, or call the Boys Town National Hotline at 1-800-448-3000 if you would like additional help with the problem.

Q. My child is being picked on by a bully at school. What do I tell him to do? Do I tell the school about the problem? Do I call the bully's parents?

A. We hope that our kids are safe at school, but that's not always the case. Also, many kids get hurt on the way to or from school or school activities. It's up to parents to teach their children how to best handle situations such as, what to do when someone tries to get your money or take your coat or bully you into doing homework for him.

Each family might approach the bully problem differently. Some parents might want their son to get tough, fight back, and quit being such a baby about the whole thing. Others might tell their son to fight back because, if he doesn't, he'll be labeled a sissy and get picked on for years to come. Still other parents might want to teach their son how to handle the problem so that he doesn't get in a fight.

There are good and bad points to each of these approaches. If you teach your child to fight back, he may truly be safer because bullies or gang members may leave him alone. You also risk that he relies on fighting to solve his other problems such as when his sister has a toy he wants or he thinks he needs another classmate's new shoes. If you teach your child to avoid fights and escape problems with the bully, he might be identified as an easy target, and others may pick on him, too. Or, he might get good at talking his way out of problems and learn to rely on his brains rather than his brawn to solve problems.

Here's one technique that has worked for parents. It's call the R.A.C.E. approach to potentially dangerous situations. R.A.C.E. stands for recognize, avoid, comebacks, and escape.

Recognize: Teach your son to recognize potentially dangerous situations. For example, when he sees the class bully with a group of the bully's friends, then he needs to recognize that problems are likely to occur. Also, teach him to recognize types of clothes, hand signals, and words that kids may use that indicate that problems are likely to happen. Teach him to recognize that certain buildings, street corners, and graffiti signal problem areas to avoid. Finally, teach him about the dangers of poorly lighted streets, tall shrubbery, or abandoned cars in which people can hide. In short, teach your child how to be street-smart when it comes to seeing problems before they happen.

Avoid: When your child spots a potentially dangerous situation, there are several things he can do to stay out of the situation. For example, if your son's walking home from school and he sees two or three teens hanging out on the corner, he may be safer if he turns down another street and takes the long way home. Whenever possible, have your son walk with a friend or several friends. Two or more kids together are always safer than being out there alone. Also, walk the route with your child to and from school. Identify the apartments or homes he can go to for help. Then talk with those living in the identified safe houses about your son's safety on the way to school. Ask them if they would be around before and after school if your son needed to run to their apartment for help.

Comebacks: Sometimes, despite all efforts, your son finds himself in a problem situation. Teach him how to think clearly at those times. In dangerous situations, it's often recommended to give the person whatever he or she asks for. In less threatening situations, teach your son to "come back" with a quick line making fun of himself. So if the bully says, "Hey punk, I thought I told you to make an extra copy of your homework for me." You could teach your son to say, "Man, I am so stupid. I didn't want you to get a bad grade so I didn't get you a copy. You can have mine if you want, but I'm sure I'm wrong on half of them." A comeback such as this may help him avoid getting hurt.

Escape: On some occasions, there are opportunities to leave the problem situation, but the child is so caught up in what's going on that he misses the chance. For example, if the bully and one of his friends get in an argument, then take the opportunity to escape the bully as quickly as possible. Teach him to head for the school building or one of the identified safe houses. Or teach him how to get adults involved without drawing attention to the bully.

For example, if your son sees a teacher, he could say, "Hey, Mr. Wilson! Want to shoot baskets with us?" This involves the teacher without having your child labeled a "narc" or tattle-tale.

You have the best information to help you answer the questions about telling the school or bully's parents. If the school has demonstrated the ability to help with these problems in the past, then school staff will likely be a big help with this problem. If they have been ineffective in the past, then still inform them of the problem, but most of the responsibility for your child's safety will fall on your shoulders. The same qualifications are true with respect to the bully's parents. If he has a responsible parent, grandparent, or other adult caring for him, then it would help a great deal to get them involved. If the adults in the bully's life are not involved with him due to drugs, alcohol, or criminal activity, then telling them will have little or no effect on the bully. It could even make matters worse for your child. Base your decision on what you think will best help your child be safe before, during, and after school.

Q. What do I do if I feel like my child is being treated unfairly by school staff?

A. Most school teachers and administrators work with children because of their commitment to children and their belief in the value of a sound education. However, school staff occasionally make mistakes like the rest of us. In those cases, if you feel that it will be helpful, then go directly to the staff involved and share your concerns. If the problem doesn't improve or if you don't feel comfortable talking directly with the staff who allegedly is treating your child unfairly, then meet with the staff's supervisor or the building principal.

Many parents have told us that they feel very upset or angry when they must talk with teachers about how their child's been treated. Others feel anxious or worry about what might happen to their child if they raise concerns about the teacher's behavior. In either case, try to get calm before going to talk with school staff. Write down your concerns. Read and rewrite where necessary to avoid comments that might be hurtful, but won't help solve the problem. Stick to the issues and avoid attacking the teacher. Some teachers are open to suggestions and input from parents, while other teachers avoid getting feedback from parents or attack the parent giving the feedback. Keep your cool, and work to solve the problem.

Earlier in this chapter, we discussed guidelines for communicating with school staff and administration. Follow those guidelines and remember to work with school staff to solve the problem. Follow school protocol, yet continue taking your concerns up the chain of command if you feel that your child's needs are not being met or if your concerns are dismissed. Stop only after you are comfortable with the outcome. Your child's education and future may be at stake.

Exercise 1 – Setting Up Study Time with Your Children

Here's an example for Emily, a 13-year-old junior high student. She gets home at approximately 4 p.m. each day and has sports practice or games several times per week. Emily's schedule also includes study time for at least one hour, five nights per week.

Time	Sunday	Monday	Tuesday	Wednesday	Thursday	Friday	Saturday
4-4:30		Soccer Practice	At Yvette's	Soccer Practice			Soccer Game
4:30-5					Soccer Game		
5-5:30							
5:30-6	Study	Study	Study	Study	Study		
6-6:30							
6:30-7							

Use the chart below to map out your children's evening schedule for the upcoming week. (Or make a similar plan that works better for your children's schedules.) Set up study time based on the amount of time recommended for the age and ability of your child. For children in the elementary grades, recommended study time is 30 to 45 minutes; for junior high students, 45 to 75 minutes; and for high school students, 60 to 90 minutes or more. Adjust these general guidelines based on your knowledge of your child's capabilities or recommendations from your child's teachers.

Time	Sunday	Monday	Tuesday	Wednesday	Thursday	Friday	Saturday
4-4:30							
4:30-5							
5-5:30							
5:30-6							
6-6:30							
6:30-7							
7-7:30							
7:30-8							
8-8:30							
8:30-9							
9-9:30							
9:30-10							

Exercise 2 – Communicating with Teachers & School Administrators

Watch the parents on the video and then pause the video. Match the steps in the right column with the words on the left that best fit each step. Then, start the video after you finish the exercise and see how your answers compare with those from the parents in class.

Scene 1

Your child has missed several homework assignments. His teacher has just called you to talk about this problem. How do you handle it?

Parent's Responses	Steps
"We'll have him start on the missed assignments tonight and be sure that he gets them turned in by Friday."	Step 1. Stay calm.
"I'll check on him each night to make sure he gets the rest of his assignments done."	Step 2. Get information.
Take a deep breath and say, "Thank you for calling."	Step 3. Take care of the problem.
"Can you tell me which assignments he's missing so I can get him to turn them in?"	Step 4. Prevent future problems.

See the section in this chapter about setting up study time for additional ideas on how to take care of this problem and prevent similar situations in the future.

Scene 2

Your child has been arguing with his teacher and making rude comments in class. Your child's teacher is meeting with you to discuss this problem. How do you handle it?

Parent's Responses	Steps
"We can use a school note to help keep track of his behavior in school."	Step 1. Stay calm.
"What's he been doing?"	Step 2. Get information.
"I'm sorry that he treated you that way in front of the whole class."	Step 3. Take care of the problem.
"Would it be all right to have him apologize to you and the whole class?"	Step 4. Prevent future problems.

Here are some additional ways of solving the problem and preventing it from occurring in the future.

➤ In the last section of this chapter, we discussed how school notes provide effective communication between parent and teacher. School notes can be very helpful in situations such as the one in this exercise, where students are causing problems several times each day.

➤ Make sure the school note includes references to arguing and making rude comments. Also, be sure to keep track of how often the child accepts his teacher's decisions, follows instructions, and expresses his opinions in class without arguing.

➤ Use Preventive Teaching to teach him how to:

  • Get his teacher's and classmates' attention without making rude comments

  • Ask questions

  • Share his opinion

  • Disagree appropriately

  • Use appropriate humor in class

Video Exercise 2

Scene 3

Your son has failed three tests in the past month. His teacher called you to tell you that the main reason he's doing so poorly is that he isn't turning in any homework assignments. How do you handle it?

Parent's Responses	Steps
"What kinds of things has my son been doing in class?"	Step 1. Stay calm.
"When he's completed his homework, I'll make sure that I go over it to make sure it's done correctly."	Step 2. Get information.
"I'll make sure to schedule a structured study time with my son."	Step 3. Take care of the problem.
"I appreciate you taking the time to meet with me about this."	Step 4. Prevent future problems.

Here are some additional ways of solving the problem and preventing it from occurring in the future.

➤ Have your son study in a room where you can be present to be sure that there are no distractions, that he has the right materials, and that he is staying on task.

➤ Have your son outline the textbook chapter on paper or 3x5 note cards.

➤ Help your son study for tests by reviewing his notes or cards with him. Ask questions from the notes and have him answer without using his book. If he has difficulty, have him look up the answer and say it to you.

➤ Since your son may not be preparing well enough for tests, check with his teacher to find out when tests are given. Then begin studying for the test one to two weeks before the test date.

➤ Teach your son how to read the chapter and pick out the main topics. Then ask him questions about those main points during the day or evening. The frequent repetition will help him remember the information at test time.

➤ Look for ways to make study time enjoyable. For example, have him invite a friend over to study with him. Or study for 30 minutes, then take 30 minutes to do something together that he enjoys. Then head back to the books for another half hour.

Job and Joy Jar Suggestions

Job Jar

Here's a list of chores that can be used in a job jar. Be sure to adapt the list to your own situation. Remember, when choosing a consequence, use the smallest consequence you think will help your child change his or her behavior. Also, be sure to match the chores to your child's age and abilities.

Small	Medium	Large
Clean out kitchen silverware drawer	Vacuum one room	Clean out kitchen junk drawer
Clean trash out of car	Put clean dishes in cabinet	Vacuum car
Clean bathroom sink	Clean bathroom toilet	Rake all or part of the yard
Clean the kitchen sink	Dust furniture in one room	Clean entire bathroom
Fold 10 pieces of laundry	Put laundry away	Fold load of laundry
Help a brother or sister put toys away	Help a brother or sister with chores	Clean out and organize the garage
Make a brother's or sister's bed	Sweep the kitchen or dining room floor	Wash, dry, and put away the dishes
Sweep the porch	Shake the rugs	Mow the grass
Take out the trash	Collect the trash	Organize a closet

Job Jar List (continued)

Small	Medium	Large
Sweep the sidewalk	Shovel the sidewalk	Wash windows in one room
Pull 10-20 weeds (approximately 10 minutes)	Pull 20-30 weeds (Approximately 20 minutes)	Clean mold off tiles in shower
Pick up litter in the yard	Clear the table	Vacuum several rooms
Clean mirror in bathroom	Clean out trash can	Scrub burner on stove
Sweep out garage	Water plants	Wash tub or shower
Set the table	Clean up the dog "dirt" in the yard	Clean out kitchen cabinet
	Wipe down kitchen cabinets	Clean the oven
	Bring firewood in	Clean out refrigerator
	Scrub outside of pots and pans	Scrub floor
	Wash the car windows (inside)	Polish furniture
		Wash windows
		Wash the car
		Clean out fireplace
		Stack the wood
		Clean the rain gutters
		Edge the grass

Joy Jar

Here's a list of reinforcers that can be used to encourage your children's positive behavior. The list is divided into three categories: Activities, People, and Food. This gives you the option of choosing certain types of reinforcers to put in your joy jar.

Activities

Free (or pretty cheap)

Go to the park

Go for a walk

Stay up 15 extra minutes

Stay outside 15 extra minutes

Leave the radio on at night

Go window shopping

Camp out in the family room

Camp out in the back yard

Stay up late reading

Sleep in late on weekend

Sit at the head of the table

Listen to music (20 min.)

Go to the library

Do one less chore

Get extra time on the computer

Get extra phone time

Messy room for a day

Play a favorite game

Stay out late (supervised)

Pick the TV program

Get extra TV (or video game) time

Cost money

Go to a ball game

Get a comic book

Get a music cassette or CD

Pick a movie (parents must approve)

Take a trip to the zoo, pet store, etc.

Food

Free (or pretty cheap)

Plan the menu

Eat dinner in the family room

Have an indoor or outdoor picnic

Decide where to go for dinner

Mom or Dad fixes a special breakfast

Fix a special snack

Pick the breakfast cereal

Cost money

Cola

Candy

Popcorn

Waffles

Granola bars

Fruit juice

Bake cookies

Popsicle

Pizza

Gum

Pop (Soda)

People

Go to a friend's house

Have a friend stay overnight

Go to Grandma's

Go for a walk with Mom or Dad

Have Mom or Dad read a story

Play game with Mom or Dad

Ride bikes with Mom or Dad

Go fishing with Mom or Dad

Special time with Mom or Dad

Have a friend over to play

Get a hug from Mom or Dad

Social Skills

Skills List*

1. How to follow instructions
2. How to say "No" to friends
3. How to accept "No" answers
4. How to ask permission
5. How to apologize
6. How to disagree appropriately
7. How to stay calm
8. How to accept a consequence or criticism
9. How to get along with others
10. How to let parents/teachers know where you are going
11. How to ask for help
12. How to dress appropriately
13. How to complete homework
14. How to join in a conversation
15. How to ask questions
16. How to manage time
17. How to be prepared for class
18. How to stay on task
19. How to be on time
20. How to get the teacher's attention
21. How to ignore distractions by others
22. How to contribute to group activities
23. How to study
24. How to wait your turn
25. How to volunteer to help
26. How to express pride in accomplishments

---

*Skills are adapted from the following Boys Town Press publications:

Burke, R., Herron, R., & Barnes, B. (2006). *Common Sense Parenting* (3rd ed.). Boys Town, NE: Boys Town Press.

Dowd, T., & Tierney, J. (2005). *Teaching Social Skills to Youth* (2nd ed.). Boys Town, NE: Boys Town Press.

Herron, R. (1996). *Getting Along with Others*. Boys Town, NE: Boys Town Press.

1.   How to Follow Instructions

How to follow instructions is one of the most important skills for a child to learn. A child who can follow instructions will be successful in school, at home, and eventually on the job. Here are the steps for following instructions:

1. **Look at the person.**
2. **Say "okay."**
3. **Do what is asked.**
4. **Check back to let the person know you are finished.**

Helpful hints to share with kids:

It is important to do what is asked because it shows your ability to cooperate and it saves time. Following instructions will help you in school, at home, and with adults and friends.

➤ After finding out exactly what has been asked, start the task immediately.

➤ If you feel that what you're being asked to do is really wrong, then ask a trusted adult what you should do.

➤ Speak clearly, and use a pleasant voice.

➤ Do the best job you can, asking for help if you have problems.

➤ When you're finished, ask if the job was done correctly, and redo anything that needs correcting.

2.   How to Say "No" to Friends

Sometimes friends can be great. But, other times friends can ask your children to do things they shouldn't do. Here's what your child can do:

1. **Say "No" and state your reason clearly.**
2. **Be persistent with your "No" answer.**
3. **Ask the person to leave you alone.**
4. **Remove yourself from the situation, if necessary.**

Helpful hints to share with kids:

➤ Friends who won't let you say "No" are not really friends.

➤ Your friends may be angry with you for saying "No," but they will probably respect your courage.

➤ If you are the one to say "No," you might make it easier for someone who didn't have the courage to speak up.

➤ When you say "No" you're likely to stay out of trouble. That means fewer problems for you, and sometimes your friends, too.

3. How to Accept "No" Answers

Children and teens will be told "No" thousands of times in their lives. If they can accept the answer they receive or disagree appropriately, they will be more likely to accomplish what they want in the long run. Here's what you can teach your children to do when they get a "No" answer.

1. **Look at the person.**
2. **Say, "Okay."**
3. **Calmly ask for a reason if you really don't understand.**
4. **If you disagree, ask to bring it up later.**

Helpful hints to share with kids:

You will be told "No" many times in your life. Getting angry and upset only leads to more problems. If you are able to appropriately accept the "No" answer, people will view you as cooperative and mature.

➤ If you get upset, try to relax and stay calm. Listening carefully will help you understand what the other person is saying.

➤ Take a deep breath if you feel upset. Then, respond to their answer right away and speak clearly.

➤ People will think you are serious about wanting to know a reason if you ask for one calmly. Don't ask for a reason every time you get told "No" or you will be viewed as a complainer.

➤ It's often best to accept the "No" answer on the spot and then go back later to ask questions or suggest another option. Use the time to plan how you are going to approach the person who told you "No." When you speak with the person a second time, be sure to accept the answer, even if it is still "No."

4. How to Ask Permission

Children need to learn that it is important to ask permission whenever they want to do something or use something that belongs to another person. Asking permission shows respect for others and increases the chances that a request will be granted.

Here are the steps for asking permission:

1. **Look at the other person.**
2. **Ask rather than demand.**
3. **Give a reason for what you want to do.**
4. **Accept the decision.**

Helpful hints to share with kids:

➤ It is always wise to ask before you use something that doesn't belong to you. It doesn't matter if it is a bag of potato chips or someone's bike: Ask permission!

➤ Sometimes you won't get what you want. But if you have asked permission politely and correctly, it is more likely that you may get what you want the next time.

➤ It may help you to think about how you would feel if someone used something of yours without asking first. Besides feeling that the other person was not polite and did not respect your property, you would be worried that the item could get broken or lost.

5. How to Apologize

When children have done something that hurts another person's feelings or results in negative consequences for another person, they should apologize. By apologizing, they show that they are sensitive to others' feelings. Here are the steps for making an apology:

1. **Look at the person.**
2. **Say what you are sorry about: "I'm sorry I said…" or "I'm sorry I was teasing you," or "I'm sorry I hit you."**
3. **Make a follow-up statement if the person says something to you: "Is there any way I can make it up to you?" or "It won't happen again."**
4. **Thank the person for listening (even if the person did not accept your apology).**

(Parents can set a good example for their children when they apologize whenever they make a mistake. This shows children that mistakes are okay, and what's really important is that we learn from our mistakes. Apologizing is the first step toward learning from mistakes, and it helps those involved recover from problems that may have resulted.)

Helpful hints to share with kids:

➤ It is easy to avoid making apologies; it takes guts to be mature enough to do it. Convince yourself that making an apology is the best thing to do, and then do it!

➤ If the other person is upset with you, the response you receive when you apologize may not be nice. Be prepared to take whatever the other person says. Be confident that you are doing the right thing when you apologize.

➤ When people look back on your apology, they will see that you were able to realize what you did wrong. They will think more positively of you in the future.

➤ An apology won't erase what you did wrong, but it may help change a person's opinion of you in the long run.

6. How to Disagree Appropriately

We often have opinions that are different from those around us. This is true of children as well as adults. Parents need to teach their children how to share those opinions in helpful ways, especially when those opinions don't match those around them. Here are the steps for disagreeing appropriately.

1. **Remain calm.**
2. **Look at the person.**
3. **Begin with a positive or neutral statement: "I know you are trying to be fair…" or "I understand what you're saying, but I think…."**
4. **Explain in a calm voice why you disagree.**
5. **Listen to the other person without interrupting.**
6. **Calmly accept whatever decision is made.**
7. **Thank the person for listening, regardless of the outcome.**

Helpful hints to share with kids:

➤ You're not going to win every time. Some decisions will not change. However, learning how to disagree calmly may help change some of them.

➤ Yelling, swearing, name-calling, and making negative comments are not part of disagreeing appropriately. Angry and mean disagreements only lead to more problems. People only hear your anger and miss your message.

➤ There is a time and place for most disagreements. And sometimes, even if it means that you can't immediately do what you want to do, the best thing is to wait until later to disagree with your parent's decision.

7. How to Stay Calm

When people feel angry or upset, it's difficult to stay calm. When children feel like "blowing up," they sometimes make poor choices. When they make poor choices, they usually say and do things they regret later. Here are the steps for staying calm:

1. **Recognize the situations that make you angry.**
2. **Take a deep breath and relax your muscles.**
3. **Tell yourself to "Be calm," or count to ten.**
4. **After you have relaxed, share your feelings with someone you trust.**
5. **Try to resolve the situation that made you upset.**

Helpful hints to share with kids:

➤ Everyone gets mad at one time or another, but if you can stay calm, other people will depend on you more often. They will see you as mature and able to handle even the worst situations. Teachers and employers will respect you and see you as someone who can keep "cool."

➤ You might try to talk yourself into the idea that "blowing up" is the only thing to do, or that the other person or thing "deserves it." Forget it. It doesn't work that way. And you're setting yourself up to get more or worse consequences.

➤ After you have calmed down, pat yourself on the back. Even adults have a hard time with self-control. If you can control yourself, you will have accomplished something that many adults are still struggling with. Give yourself some praise! You have done the right thing.

8. How to Accept a Consequence or Criticism

Children often get upset when parents give them a consequence or criticism. They argue, fight, have tantrums, and do whatever might help them avoid consequences or listen to criticism. One way to help them benefit from consequences and criticism is to teach them these steps:

1. **Look at the person.**
2. **Stay calm and quiet while the person is talking.**
3. **Show you understand with "okay" or "I understand."**
4. **Try to correct the problem.**

It is important for children to avoid arguing and stay calm when they get consequences or criticism. They may not like to hear that they have done something wrong, but the best they can do at that point is to learn what they can do in the future to avoid the misbehavior or mistake.

Helpful hints to share with kids:

➤ It is most important that you stay calm. Take a deep breath, if necessary.

➤ When you respond to the person who is giving you criticism or a consequence, use as pleasant a voice as possible. You will receive consequences and criticism for the rest of your life: All people do. The way you handle it determines how you are treated by others.

➤ Most consequences and criticism are designed to help you; however, sometimes they are hard to accept. If you don't understand or agree with the consequence or criticism, ask to talk about it at another time, but don't play games by asking questions when you do understand and are just being stubborn.

9.   How to Get Along with Others

To be successful in dealing with people, you should:

1. **Listen to what is being said when another person talks to you.**
2. **Say something positive if you agree with what that person said.** *(If you don't agree, say something that won't cause an argument.)*
3. **Show interest in what the other person has to say.** *(Try to understand his or her point of view.)*

Helpful hints to share with kids:

It's important to get along with others because you will be working and dealing with other people all of your life. If you can get along with others, it is more likely that you will be successful in whatever you do. Getting along shows sensitivity and respect. In other words, treat others the way you want to be treated!

➤ Sometimes it's not easy to get along with others. If your friend (or more likely, your brother or sister) does something that you don't like, or says something negative, you may feel like saying something nasty or unpleasant. Don't! Stop yourself from saying things that can hurt others' feelings. Teasing, cussing, and insults will only make matters worse. It is better to ignore others' negative behavior than to act like them.

➤ Getting along with others takes some effort. It's hard to understand why some people act the way they do. Try to see things from their point of view and maybe their behavior will be easier to understand.

➤ If you find that you don't like what someone says or does, it's better to say nothing rather than something negative.

10. How to Let Parents/Teachers Know Where You Are Going

It is important to know where your children are and what they are doing. This is true, no matter how old they are. Knowing where your children are helps keep them safe and out of trouble.

1. **Tell whoever is taking care of you where you're going.** *(Most of the time, you should ask rather than tell if you'd like to go somewhere.)*
2. **Be sure you go where you said you would.**
3. **Let the person know if you change your mind and go somewhere else.**
4. **Check in with the person when you return.**

Helpful hints to share with kids:

➤ When adults know where you are, they can let you know when a friend calls, find you in an emergency, call you for dinner, or let you know that you've won the lottery! It pays to let adults know.

➤ When you show that you can be responsible and let parents or other adults know where you are, you'll be likely to get to do more things on your own. If people can depend on you, they are more likely to trust you – and trust leads to opportunity.

➤ Be sure to let people know if your plans change. It only takes a minute to call and tell someone where you're going.

➤ Parents, teachers, or other adults who may be responsible for your safety get very worried if they don't know where you are. Don't go somewhere without getting permission or letting an adult know.

11. How to Ask for Help

We all run into problems at times that we can't solve alone. It can be tough admitting that we need help, but sometimes that's the most effective way to get a problem solved. Children who learn these steps are more likely to get the help they need:

1. **Look at the person when you ask for help.**
2. **Ask the person if he or she has time to help you (now or later).**
3. **Clearly describe the problem or what kind of help you need.**
4. **Thank the person for helping you.**

Helpful hints to share with kids:

➤ It is nice to figure things out on your own, but sometimes it isn't possible. One way to solve that problem is to ask someone who has more experience or success in a similar situation.

➤ Asking for help in a pleasant manner makes it more likely that someone will help you.

➤ Sometimes, people become frustrated or angry when they can't figure something out. Learn to ask for help before you get to this point, and you will have more successes than failures.

➤ Tell the person who is helping you how much you appreciate the help. It might be nice to offer your help the next time that person needs something.

12. How to Dress Appropriately

People judge us according to our appearance. It is important to dress appropriately so we don't send the wrong message, or so we are taken seriously. Here are the steps for dressing appropriately:

1. **Think about what situations and activities you will be involved in that day.**
2. **Choose clothing that suits the season.**
3. **Match colors and styles.** *(Ask your parent or trusted adult for his or her opinion about how you're dressed.)*
4. **Do not wear clothing that is too revealing or associated with gang activities.**
5. **Care for your clothing throughout the day. Do not cut, tear, or write on clothing.**

Helpful hints to share with kids:

➤ Good hygiene (for example, showering and washing your hair) and neatness (for example, wearing clothes that aren't wrinkled) are part of dressing appropriately.

➤ When in doubt, dress "up" rather than "down."

➤ You may not always agree with how your parents dress or how they ask you to dress, but they generally have good ideas about what clothes to wear for certain occasions. Take their advice and dress as they ask at those times.

➤ When you are dressed appropriately, people will feel they are being treated with respect and will in turn treat you with respect.

13. How to Complete Homework

Homework, like many daily tasks and chores, isn't always tops on a child's list of "fun" things to do. But learning to tackle homework promptly and efficiently is a skill that will help children throughout life. Here are the steps for completing homework:

1. **Find out at school what the day's homework is for each subject.**
2. **Remember to bring home necessary books or materials in order to complete your assignments.**
3. **Get started on homework at the designated time.**
4. **Complete all assignments neatly and to the best of your ability.**
5. **Carefully store completed homework until the next school day.**

Helpful hints to share with kids:

➤ If you do your homework without whining or resisting, you'll have more time and energy for other activities.

➤ Doing your homework early in the evening means you'll be sharper and more likely to do the assignment correctly.

➤ If you have a big project or assignment, start on it right away. Break it up into small tasks and check each one off the list as you complete it. Generally, students who start their assignments right away get better grades on their work than students who wait until the last minute to get started.

➤ Expect the unexpected! If you allow plenty of time and start your homework early, an unexpected problem or emergency won't mean not finishing your assignment.

14. How to Join in a Conversation

Children sometimes feel uncomfortable sharing their ideas when their friends or classmates are talking with each other. When children can become part of the conversation, they are more likely to make friends, share ideas, and feel confident when called on in class. Here's how children can join in a conversation:

1. **Look at the people who are talking.**
2. **Answer any questions asked of you.**
3. **If no one asks you a question, wait for a time when no one else is talking.**
4. **Make a short, appropriate comment that relates to the topic being discussed.** *(You can also ask a question about the topic, talk about a new event, or ask one of the others what they think about the topic.)*
5. **After you talk, give others a chance to participate.**

Helpful hints to share with kids:

➤ Give complete answers: Just saying "yes" or "no" does not give the other person any information that can keep the conversation going.

➤ Always include the other person's ideas in the conversation. If you don't, it won't be a conversation!

➤ Smile, and show interest in what the other person has to say, even if you don't agree with it.

➤ Keep up on current events so that you have a wide range of things to talk about. People who can talk about what's happening and are good at conversation are usually liked and admired by other people.

15. How to Ask Questions

Children who ask questions in school or at home are more likely to understand what others are telling them. Unfortunately, children often make the mistake of asking "why" questions instead of "how" questions. For example, when you ask your 12-year-old to take out the trash, he mistakenly asks, "Why do I have to?" That's a question you've probably answered hundreds of times already.

If he has questions, they should be "how" questions, such as, "How do you want it done" or "How soon do you want it done?" The same is true in school.

When the teacher asks your daughter to do ten problems in math for homework, questions such as, "How would I do number eight?" will be more helpful than, "Why do I have to do these problems?" Here's how your children can ask "how" questions:

1. **Look at the other person to get his or her attention politely and without interrupting. Wait until he or she sees you.**
2. **In a pleasant tone of voice, ask the question using words such as "how," "please," "would you," "what," or "may I...."**
3. **Listen to the person's answer.**
4. **Thank the person for his or her time.**

Helpful hints to share with kids:

➤ Most people are flattered, not annoyed, by being asked questions.

➤ You actually appear *(and are!)* smarter for asking questions.

➤ Asking questions of others helps them feel comfortable asking you questions.

➤ Questions keep a conversation moving.

16. How to Manage Time

Most of us have so many demands on our time that, unless we manage activities, our lives get chaotic. Children and teens lead busy lives, too. It is helpful when they can learn to plan ahead and organize their activities. When students can organize their time, they're more likely to get school assignments completed and turned in on time. Here are some steps for managing time:

1. **List all tasks for a particular day or week.**
2. **Estimate the time needed to complete each task.**
3. **Plan for delays, setbacks, and problems.**
4. **Mark on a calendar or notepad times that you will work on each task.**
5. **Work on the task when scheduled.**
6. **When you finish a task, check to see how well you managed your time. Use this information to help you organize future tasks.**

Helpful hints to share with kids:

➤ Spending a few minutes planning activities saves hours of wasted time later.

➤ Sometimes it helps to do the not-so-fun tasks first so that you get them out of the way. When you save them to the end, they hang over your head like a dark cloud. Once you've finished the not-so-fun tasks, you have more time for pleasant activities.

➤ You will accomplish much more with good time management.

17. How to Be Prepared for Class

Being prepared for class helps a child gain confidence and learn more effectively. Here are the steps for being prepared for class:

1. **Assemble all books, papers, homework, and pens or pencils.**
2. **Be on time for class.**
3. **Present homework and assignments when requested by the teacher.**
4. **Write down assignments.**

Helpful hints to share with kids:

➤ If you're prepared, you will likely do better in class and your teacher will take you and your work more seriously.

➤ If some type of emergency does happen so that you're not ready for class, your teacher will probably be more understanding based on your history.

➤ Being prepared means you have yesterday's lesson mastered so that today's will be much easier to understand.

18. How to Stay on Task

Learning to concentrate is a difficult skill for many children – and adults – to master. However, contrary to what many people think, it is a skill that can be learned. Here's how it's done:

1. **Look at your task or assignment.**
2. **Think about the steps needed to complete the task.**
3. **Focus all of your attention on your task.**
4. **Stop working on your task only with permission of the adult who gave you the task.**
5. **Ignore distractions and interruptions by others.**

Helpful hints to share with kids:

➤ If you're at home, pick a quiet spot to do your tasks. The fewer distractions (such as TV or music), the more likely you will stay on task. Use classical music (without words) or soft constant sound, such as a fan or soft static from a radio, to help block out other noises around you. This makes it easier to stay focused on your task.

➤ If you're trying to stay on task at school, try holding your hands around your eyes (like blinders on a horse) so that your classmates don't distract you. Keep your eyes on the book or paper in front of you. If you continue to be distracted by your classmates, it might help to ask your teacher to move you to the front of the room where there will be fewer distractions.

➤ Staying on task means you'll finish more quickly and get back to activities you enjoy.

➤ Kids who have learned to stay on task usually win their teachers', coaches', boss's, and others' respect and often are given more responsibility.

19. How to Be on Time

Being on time shows that you respect someone else's time enough to be prompt. It's not difficult to learn this skill, but it does take some effort. These are the steps:

1. **Know when you need to be at your destination, and how long it will take you to get there.**
2. **Leave with plenty of time to spare** (*usually about 5-10 minutes before you would have to leave*).
3. **Go directly to your destination.**
4. **When you arrive, check in with someone in authority or the person you are meeting.**
5. **If you are late, apologize sincerely.**

Helpful hints to share with kids:

➤ Be aware of how long it takes to get ready, so you'll know how much time to allow.

➤ If you find you're going to be late, call the person who's waiting for you, if possible.

➤ If you have to get up early to be somewhere on time, use an alarm clock. This also works to remind you if you're busy with an activity.

20. How to Get the Teacher's Attention

Children spend a large part of their lives in the classroom. It's important for them to be able to interact appropriately with their teachers. One important skill they need to learn is how to get their teacher's attention:

1. **Look at your teacher.**
2. **Raise your hand calmly.**
3. **Wait until your teacher calls on you.**
4. **Ask your question or give the answer in a calm voice.**
5. **If your teacher answers your question, thank him or her.**

Helpful hints to share with kids:

➤ Remember, you are only one of your teacher's many students. Wait patiently while your teacher is helping someone else or while someone else is answering a question.

➤ If you fail to get the teacher's attention the first time, try again.

➤ If you often have trouble getting your teacher's attention, speak with him or her during a break or between classes. Explain the situation and ask how you should get their attention.

21. How to Ignore Distractions by Others

Kids sometimes argue that they can do homework, concentrate on what you're saying, or stay on task, no matter what the noise level is. In fact, they may argue that they need the music or TV, or friends around, just to be able to concentrate. In spite of their claims, however, noise or distractions by others do tend to lessen children's abilities to concentrate. How, then, can they learn to concentrate in the middle of an active classroom? Here are some steps they can take:

1. **Try not to look at people who are being distracting.**
2. **Stay focused on your work or task.**
3. **Do not respond to questions, teasing, or giggling.**
4. **If necessary, report distracting behavior to a nearby authority figure.**

Helpful hints to share with kids:

➤ If you practice concentrating when you have few or no distractions, you'll do much better when you're in a place with many distractions.

➤ If someone repeatedly tries to bother you, ignore that person. He or she will eventually give up.

➤ Learning how to concentrate takes practice. Stick with it, even if you are easily distracted, at first.

➤ Sometimes, students feel uncomfortable telling the teacher during class about a classmate who is causing problems. When that happens, talk with the teacher outside of class and explain the situation.

22. How to Contribute to Group Activities

It's no fun being left out, but sometimes children don't quite know how to go about joining in, or they're too shy to ask to be included. Here are some steps that might help them feel more comfortable contributing to group activities:

1. **Ask in a pleasant voice to join an activity.**
2. **Ask what role you can play** (*or offer to take a role that sounds like you'd enjoy it*)*.*
3. **Do your part completely.**
4. **Cooperate with others by listening, sharing your ideas, and accepting their ideas.**
5. **Say something nice to others when they do well.**

Helpful hints to share with kids:

➤ Try to remember that we're all a little uncomfortable when it comes to joining a group. Everyone who's in the group now was once just where you are.

➤ Plan ahead how you can contribute to the activity. Being prepared will give you confidence.

➤ If you don't have success the first time, try again at another time or with a different group or activity.

➤ Sometimes, groups try to get you to do things that are wrong or dangerous. When that happens, get away from the group as quickly as possible. Call your parent or tell your teacher if someone tries to get you to do something that is wrong.

23. How to Study

Good study skills are essential if a child is going to do well, both in elementary and high school. College is even more demanding. Studies have shown that students who study and complete homework on a regular basis do much better in school than those who do not study outside of class time. The following points can help your child learn how to study:

1. **Assemble necessary books and materials.**
2. **Focus your attention on the required work.**
3. **Make notes of important facts.**
4. **Repeat important points to yourself several times.**
5. **Remain on task, free from distractions** *(no radio or TV).*

Helpful hints to share with kids:

➤ Don't wait until the last minute to study. You need to allow plenty of time.

➤ Take a break and stretch if you have been studying and feel groggy or find yourself reading the same material over and over. Sometimes, it's helpful to plan breaks ahead of time. That way you'll be more likely to concentrate on your work for 15 minutes if you know you'll be taking a break soon.

➤ Don't listen to friends who try to convince you that studying isn't important or cool. Make the decisions that are best for you and for your future.

➤ Studying helps you to be more prepared, which makes you more confident.

24. How to Wait Your Turn

Nobody likes to stand in line, wait to be called on, or be put on hold on the telephone, but sometimes we have to be patient and just wait. It's a tough lesson for adults, and even harder for kids. Here's how it's done:

1. **Sit or stand quietly.** *(Keep your arms and legs still. Also, avoid sighing, whining, or begging.)*
2. **When the person in charge calls on you, take your turn at the activity.**
3. **Thank the person who gives you a turn.**

Helpful hints to share with kids:

➤ Maybe you've heard the old saying, "The squeaky wheel gets the grease." It means that the person who make the most noise gets picked first. That often works when you're on the playground or choosing teams with your friends. But when it comes to waiting to be called on at school or waiting in line at a store, the people who wave their arms and pester often get in trouble or ignored.

➤ If you wait quietly and politely, you may get waited on more quickly.

➤ If you're at a party or just playing at a friend's house and you wait patiently, you're more likely to get invited back. Waiting patiently for your turn at a game or activity is something that parents notice. Parents are glad to invite their child's friends over to the home when those friends have good manners.

25. How to Volunteer to Help

Volunteering not only helps others, but it also gets things done more quickly because everyone is doing something to help. Volunteering can give your child a sense of confidence and satisfaction for helping. People appreciate having others help because it makes their jobs easier. Here are the steps for volunteering to help:

1. **Notice when someone is having a hard time.**
2. **Look at the person.**
3. **Ask if you can help.** *(Use a clear, enthusiastic voice.)*
4. **Let the person know when you're finished with the task.**

Helpful hints to share with kids:

➤ Follow through with what you volunteered to do. People will see you as responsible when you do.

➤ Even if you're not sure how much you can help, don't be afraid to ask, "Is there anything I can do to help?"

➤ Be enthusiastic and have fun when helping others. Everyone will benefit.

26. How to Express Pride in Accomplishments

It's exciting to do things well! We all want to be able to enjoy our successes and share that joy with others. There are ways to do that without bragging or making others feel left out. It takes sensitivity and some practice. Following are the steps children can take to express pride in their accomplishments in an appropriate way.

1. **Look at the person you are talking to.**
2. **Describe what you did and how happy you are.** *(Use an enthusiastic voice.)*
3. **Be careful not to brag or put others down.**

Helpful hints to share with kids:

➤ It's okay to feel good about and share your successes with others.

➤ Be sensitive to others' feelings. You hurt other's feelings when you put them down to make yourself look better.

➤ Remember to praise others for their accomplishments, too.

Index

A

accentuate the positive, 25
accepting "no" answers, 52, 53, 59-60, 151
accomplishments, how to express
    pride in, 167
activities, as consequence, 12
activity, 6, 7, 24, 48, 50, 53, 61, 68
    affection, 24
    communication, 7
    Corrective Teaching, 68
    discipline, 6
    praise, 24
    Preventive Teaching, 48, 50, 53
    social skills, teaching, 61
affection, showing, 23
agreements, 30-39
    examples, 31-38
anger, handling, 116
apologizing, 93-94, 152
approval, show your, 26
arguments, stopping, 80
asking for help, 127, 157
    with homework, 127
asking permission, 60-61, 83-84, 122, 151-152
asking questions, 159-160

attention, as consequence, 12
avalanche trap, 15
avoidance (RACE approach), 138

B

Barnes, B., 149
bedtime routine, 40, 54
    agreement, 34
behavior, 6, 7, 8-15, 19, 21, 23-39, 47-63,
    67-76, 90, 91, 129-131
    definition of, 6
    descriptions of, 7, 19, 21, 26
    correcting problem, 67-76
    homework, 21
    misbehavior, preventing, 47-63
    positive, encouraging, 23-29
    problem, 90, 91, 129-131
    using consequences to change, 8-15
Boys Town National Hotline, 3, 63, 116, 137
bribes, 12, 40
bullies, 137-138
Burke, R., 149

C

calming down, 94, 95-96, 98, 101, 103, 106,

109-110, 111, 115, 118

charts and contracts, 29-39, 126

  examples, 30-38

    charts, 30, 31, 32, 33, 34, 35, 36

    contracts, 37, 38

  helpful hints, 39

  reaching goals with, 29-30

  steps to, 30

chores, list of, 10

cigarettes, smoking, 117

comebacks (RACE approach), 138

Common Sense Parenting®, 2, 6, 149

communication, 6-7, 128-134, 141-143, 159

  joining a conversation, 159

  with teachers and school

    administrators, 128-134

    exercise, 141-143

consequences, 8-18, 20, 21, 69-70, 74, 83,

  97, 113, 154-155

  accepting, 154-155

  choosing, 13-14, 21, 74, 83

  chores, 10-11

  don't work, 14-15

  helpful hints, 15-16

  homework, 21, 22

  negative, 8-11

    chores, adding, 10

  older teens, 18

  positive, 11-13

    list of, 13

    types of, 12

  questions and answers, 17-18

  using to change behavior, 8-15

contracts, 37-39

Corrective Teaching, 67-76, 80-87, 100, 109-111

  activity, 68

  examples, 71-74, 100, 109, 110-111

  exercise, 80-86

  helpful hints, 74-75

  homework, 87

  steps for, 69-70

  when to use, 68

curfew agreement, 38

D

destructive children, 116

disagree, how to, 153

discipline, 5-6, 137

  activity, 6

distractions, how to ignore, 163-164

Dowd, T., 149

dressing appropriately, 157-158

drinking problem, 109-110

drug prevention, 63

E

education, parental involvement, 122-123

Effective Praise, 24-29

  definition of, 24

  examples, 26-28

  helpful hints, 28-29

  steps for, 26-27

emotionally intense situations, 89-119

empathy, definition of, 95

escape (RACE approach), 138

examples, 30-38, 51-54, 56-61, 71-74, 98-112

  charts, 30, 31, 32, 33, 34, 35, 36

  contracts, 37, 38

  Corrective Teaching, 71-74, 100, 109, 110-111

  Preventive Teaching, 51, 52, 53, 54

  social skills, teaching, 56-61

  Teaching Self-Control, 98-112

exercises, 19-20, 42-44, 64, 80-86, 118,

  140-143

  behavior, 19, 42

  calm, staying, 118

  communication with teacher and

    school administrators, 141-143

  Corrective Teaching, 80-86

  consequences, 20

  Effective Praise, 43-44

  homework, scheduling, 140

  social skills, teaching, 64

F

fighting with siblings, 77, 79, 85, 98

follow instructions, how to, 56-57, 86, 150

follow-up teaching, 96-97, 99, 101-102,

  104-105, 107-108, 110, 112, 113

food, as consequence, 12

Franklin, Ben, 47

G

general praise, 13, 24
get along with others, how to, 155
Getting Along with Others, 149
Grandma's Rule, 14
group activities, how to contribute, 164

H

helpful hints, 15, 16, 28-29, 39, 54-55, 62,
    74-75, 93-94, 113-114
    charts and contracts, 39
    consequences, delivering, 15, 16
    Corrective Teaching, 74-75
    Effective Praise, 28-29
    Preventive Teaching, 54-55
    social skills, teaching, 62
    staying calm, 93-94
    Teaching Self-Control, 113
Herron, R., 149
homework, 36-37, 123-125, 135, 136,
    140, 143, 165
    asking for help, 127
    completing, 158
    contracts, 36-37
    helping with, 126-127, 135, 136, 143
    location, establish, 123
    scheduling, 123-125, 140
    study, how to, 165
    study time activities, 124
    watching TV instead, 86, 106-108
homework, workbook activities, 21, 22, 65, 87
    behaviors, 21
    consequences, 21, 22
    Corrective Teaching, 87
    Preventive Teaching, 65
    Teaching Self-Control, 119

I

"Instead of..." phrase, 96

J

job jar, 11, 145-146
joy jar, 11, 147

K

kicking, 77

L

Learn-At-Home Kit, 3
lying, 79

M

manage time, how to, 160-161
misbehavior, preventing, 47-63
morning routine, agreement, 31

N

negative consequences, 8-11
    chores, 10

O

older teens, consequences, 18

P

people, as consequence, 12
permissions, 60-61, 83-84, 122, 151-152
physical actions, be aware of, 113
positive behavior, encouraging, 23-29
positive consequences, 11-13
positive thinking, practice, 93
possessions, as consequence, 12
praise, 23-29
    effective, 24-29, 43-44
    general, 23-24
    giving, 40-41
prepare for class, how to, 161
preventive prompt, 55
Preventive Teaching, 47-55, 125
    activity, 48, 50, 53
    examples, 51, 52, 53, 54
    helpful hints, 54-55
    homework, 65, 125
    steps for, 50
    when to use, 48-49
privileges, 9. See also consequences.
problem behaviors, correcting, 67-76, 90
    in school, 129-131
punishment, 6

Q

questions for teachers, 129
questions from parents, 17-18, 40-41, 63, 77-79, 115-117, 135-139

R

R.A.C.E. approach, 138
reasons, giving, 26-27, 50
recognition (RACE approach), 138
rewards, 12, 27. See also consequences.

S

say "no" to friends, how to, 58-59, 150
schools, 121-143
    activities, attending, 128, 135
    communication with teachers and
administrators, 128-134, 139
    discipline, 137
    helping children to succeed, 121-143
    home activities, 121-127
    homework, 123-127, 135, 136, 143
    notes to parents, 131-134, 142
        examples, 132-133
    problems, solving, 129-131
    rudeness, handling, 142
    skipping, 136
    suspensions, 136-137
    transitions, 134
screaming, how to handle, 79, 116
sleeping late, 77
smoking cigarettes, 117
social skills, teaching, 55-62, 64, 122
    accepting "no" answers, 59-60
    activity, 61
    asking permission, 60-61, 122
    examples, 56-61
    exercise, 64
    follow instructions, how to, 56-57, 122
    helpful hints, 62
    say "no" to friends, 58-59
    school list, 122
social skills list, 149-167
spanking, 116
spoiled child, 14

stay on task, how to, 161-162
staying calm, 90-94, 154
    helpful hints, 93-94
    plan for, 92-93
    steps to, 90-92
stealing, 58-59, 81-82
    correction, 81-82
    prevention, 58-59
study time, 124, 140
    activities, 124
    setting up, 140
suspensions from school, 136-137

T

take five rule, 93
tantrums, 90, 115. See also calming down.
teacher's attention, how to get, 163
teachers, questions for, 129
Teaching Self-Control, 94-114
    calming down, 95-96, 98, 101, 103,
        106, 109-110, 111
    examples, 98-112
    follow-up teaching, 96-97, 99, 101-102,
        104-105, 107-108, 110, 112
    helpful hints, 113-114
    homework, 119
    steps for, 95-97
    when to use, 94-95
Teaching Social Skills to Youth, 149
Tierney, J., 149
time, 160-161, 162
    be on time, how to, 162
    manage, how to, 160-161
time-outs, 8-9
TV watching, 86, 106-108

V

volunteering, 166

W

waiting your turn, 165-166
warning signals, recognizing, 91

Y

yelling, how to handle, 79, 116

Book Credits

Production	Russ Cappello
Page Composition	Anne Hughes
...er	Margie Utesch and Anne Hughes
...rations	Bill Colrus